ABC's OF FLUID POWER

ABC's OF FLUID POWER

by

HARRY L. STEWART

and

JOHN M. STORER

With a specially written chapter for
the guidance of the English reader
by W. Oliver (G3XT)

FOULSHAM-SAMS

TECHNICAL BOOKS

Published and distributed by

W. FOULSHAM & CO. LTD.

SLOUGH   BUCKS   ENGLAND

W. FOULSHAM & CO. LTD.

Yeovil Road, Slough, Bucks, England

ABC's OF FLUID POWER

Introduction Printed and Made in Great Britain
by East Midland Printing Company Limited, King's Lynn.
Balance printed in U.S.A.

In this electronic age, one is apt to assume that anything which is not electronic must be old-fashioned.

Fluid power is certainly old-established, since it has its roots way back in history. But it could hardly be considered old-fashioned, for it is currently being developed and utilized as an alternative to electronic techniques in some of the latest computer applications.

This is only one of many daily uses for this source of power or energy. In fact most people make use of fluid power in some form or other in the course of their everyday life. But despite the vital part that it plays in so many of their day-to-day activities (for example, in the control and braking systems of motor vehicles), comparatively few people seem to take an active interest in fluid power, unless their work gives them occasion to do so.

Perhaps this is partly because fluid power may lack the fascination and almost romantic atmosphere that surrounds electronics in its more spectacular branches—such as round-the-world short-wave radio, colour television, telemetry from outer space, electronic computer "magic" and so on: In comparison with these technical "miracles", fluid power may seem a rather more prosaic subject to the average person who has not had occasion to study it.

This book will help you to appreciate the importance of fluid power and the ways in which it is being harnessed to the needs of civilisation today in science, in industry and in the home.

Present day applications of fluid power are many and various. But they may be less spectacular than a pioneer achievement such as the hydro-electric scheme which harnessed the gigantic fluid power of Niagara Falls.

The flow of electric currents along a conductor has often been compared, in elementary explanations of basic electricity, to the flow of fluid along a pipe. The analogy is quite a sound one, provided that it is not pressed too far. It is therefore hardly surprising that fluid power can be put to a number of uses which are similar to those of electrical or electronic devices.

Functions such as amplification and switching, which are normally associated with electronic devices, can also be carried out by modern fluid systems. The latter may, in fact, offer certain advantages over their electronic counterparts.

At present the main difference in the comparative performance of electronic and fluid systems is in regard to speed. Electronic devices, especially computer systems, can be made to operate at incredible speed which nothing else can match. But there are, of course, various applications in which extreme speed of operation is not at all essential; and in these fields alternative systems can be put to good use.

As the present book originates from the United States, the various typical examples of fluid power appliances, such as hydraulic cylinders, motors, control valves, hydraulic pumps and so on, which are shown in the illustrations are of American manufacture.

Naturally there are many similar appliances and devices to be found among the products of British and European manufacturing firms which specialize in this class of equipment. In some cases the designs incorporated originate from the Continent but the machines are available on the British market. For instance, one series of high-output hydraulic motors are of Swedish design and are manufactured in Britain.

If one is endeavouring to trace sources of supply for fluid power equipment, one should bear in mind that some items are made by firms specializing exclusively or almost exclusively in this class of production, while other items are produced in the mechanical engineering divisions of firms whose names are more commonly associated with, say, electronics, computers and so on.

Preface

This book explains the basic principles of fluid power and fluid-power devices, including both hydraulic (oil) and pneumatic (air) equipment. The applied principles and practical features of hydraulic and pneumatic power devices are discussed in detail.

Since garage auto lifts, gas and oil heating equipment, pumps, and many more devices that employ hydraulic or pneumatic components have become so commonplace in our daily lives, the need for more familiarity with the fundamental principles of fluid power has intensified. A more basic knowledge of fluid-power components has become necessary as these devices have been incorporated into the ever-broadening areas of industry, agriculture, and household appliances.

Man has schemed, designed, invented, and adapted for centuries in attempting to harness the physical phenomena that are capable of expanding his power, creativity, and productivity. The use of hydraulic and pneumatic power devices is only one phase in man's effort to maintain dominance of his daily world. A fundamental understanding of these "building blocks" of automation can enhance his capacity for dominance —whether the field of engineering, industrial production, mechanics, maintenance, or even recreation is pursued.

HARRY L. STEWART
JOHN M. STORER

Contents

CHAPTER 5

CHAPTER 6

CHAPTER 7

CHAPTER 8

CHAPTER 9

CHAPTER 10

1

Historical Background of Fluid Power

The term *fluid power* has come into popular usage only in recent years. It encompasses the utilization and application of both liquids and gases as transmitting media for energy. In the transmitting of energy, considerable flexibility is inherent in fluid media, permitting simple and efficient conversion from one form of energy to another; from one type of motion to another; and from a given force to either a magnified force or a reduced force, with a complete range of control.

The use of fluid power as a tool goes back many years into the history of man's efforts to place the forces of nature into a harness of his own making. The earliest records of such utilization invariably involve the use of water both as a source of power and as a transmitting medium of the energies of nature stored therein. Since water possesses a favorable weight factor that results in motion and since its extreme mobility allows it to respond to the natural forces of gravity, one of man's earliest conquests of power was the harnessing of this latent force of water in motion by the invention and use of the simple waterwheel. Although the waterwheel is not a new invention, it has long served the needs of man and is still doing so today (Fig. 1-1). Subsequent refinements and variations have produced a sophistication that might confuse and confound the original users, but who can say that those first crude, inefficient gadgets are not largely responsible for the modern harnesses that tame and utilize the tremendous forces of the Niagara and Colorado rivers.

Fig. 1-1. Overshot type of water wheel.

The preceding paragraph has dealt with *hydraulic power* identified in its original concept. The term *hydraulic* is derived from the Greek word for water, and originally pertained to the study and use of that fluid. It was near the end of the 17th century that Torricelli, Mariotte, and, later, Bernoulli carried on experiments to study the elements of pressure or force in the discharge of water through orifices in the sides of tanks and through short pipes. In the same period the French scientist, Blaise Pascal, evolved the fundamental law for the science of hydraulics.

It was more than one hundred years later that mechanical gadgetry was developed that led to the subsequent application of these theories to industrial production. Although these early developments may appear crude today in the Space Age, they gave birth to such modern components as the hydraulic pump and, in turn, the accumulator. It is interesting to note at this point that both the basic accumulator and the simple hydraulic pump preceded the use of electric power and the development of the electric motor.

Originally, the simple hydraulic pump was used with quite limited success, due to the inherent problems of matching both volume and pressure with the work requirements. With the development of the accumulator as a chamber for the storing of energy and for delivering this stored energy on demands in excess of the mechanical pumping rate, a refinement was thus created that prompted many observers of the late 19th century to conclude that the science of hydraulics had reached its ultimate maturity. The wildest dreamers of that day would be completely flabbergasted by the almost endless number of uses of fluid power that are now enjoyed by the vast majority of industrial and nonindustrial people throughout today's society. A brief look at some of the everyday encounters with fluid power might stagger even the imagination of the uninformed people who are almost totally unaware of the myriad items that daily serve the needs and comforts of our modern society.

The touch of a button or lever transmits dozens of horsepower units to the rubber-clad wheels that propel our automobiles and other vehicles. The touch of a pedal converts foot power to braking power that brings a vehicle in motion to a controlled stop. The application of vacuum power to that same pedal further multiplies that foot power in the form of power brakes. Hydraulic power is used to hoist the vehicle to make its working parts accessible for maintenance and repair. Stepping on a rubber mat at the supermarket may trigger fluid power for opening the door for the laden customer. Bank-vault doors, blast-protection doors, and huge radiation-protection doors weighing several tons are controlled by simply pressing a button or a switch. The average American farm today is blessed with hydraulic muscles as a basic part of the common tractor. Plows, mowing equipment, cultivators, and many other farm implements and attachments are hydraulically controlled or powered (Fig. 1-2). Today's farmer does many things with fluid power muscles—from digging the post holes to milking the cows.

As the vehicles of land, sea, air, and space become larger, heavier, and more complex, hydraulic power becomes even more necessary and commonplace to guide, control, and modulate them. Barber chairs, dental chairs, hospital beds, freight elevators, truck tailgates, railroad crossing gates, construction equipment (Fig. 1-3), highway maintenance equipment (Fig. 1-4), and even the tarpaulins in some baseball stadiums are made functional by the application of fluid power, and the listing has only begun. The average member of today's society may not be fluid power conscious, but he is, unquestionably, enjoying its benefits.

Courtesy International Harvester Company

Fig. 1-2. Hydraulically controlled loader attachment for a farm tractor.

This universal application of fluid power is due to the efforts of many creative men and to the design, development, and experimental facilities of many fluid power component manufacturers. As the need for greater efficiencies arose, better and more efficient seals were developed. As greater ambient and operating temperature variations were encountered, synthetic fluids and sealing compounds were developed to make such fluid power applications practical. The demand for greater forces and for space conservation has led to the continuing increase of operating pressures and the development of smaller, but more powerful, components. Control valves

Fig. 1-3. An application of fluid power in construction equipment.

have been developed that can provide a degree of precision and flexibility never dreamed of by the preceding generation of fluid power users. The servo valve has been refined to a degree that enables the precision factor to nearly overshadow the

Fig. 1-4. An application of fluid power in construction and maintenance equipment.

Courtesy Holan Corporation

11

factor of power flexibility, and it has opened the door to tape and punch card control of entire production sequences (Fig. 1-5). Fluid power controlled machines which provide for programming complete series of machining operations by merely

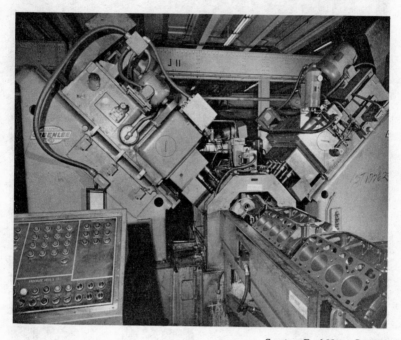

Courtesy Ford Motor Company

Fig. 1-5. Application of fluid power in this 11-station transfer machine. Three built-in turnover fixtures position the cylinder blocks correctly for tapping all the holes in the V-8 cylinder block. There are 109 spindles in action.

inserting a control tape into the control console of the machine are now being produced and marketed. Such sophistication, however, is beyond the scope of this text.

World War II created a veritable explosion in the expansion of fluid power applications. Aircraft landing gear and control surfaces were manipulated by fluid power, and complete aircraft were launched at sea by fluid powered catapults. Giant guns utilized fluid power to control both azimuth and elevation. Ground support equipment not only incorporated a great variety of fluid power components and applications, but, in turn, contributed greatly to the rapidly expanding and growing science of fluid power. In pre-World War II days, only a few manufacturers of fluid power components existed in this country. Today, there are literally hundreds of manufacturers, ranging from the builders of a specialized component to a few manufacturers of the complete systems.

Probably the most significant users of fluid power components have been in the field of production machinery. As a result of the industry's concern for uniformity of quality and performance specifications, representatives of fluid power equipment manufacturers, machine tool builders, and related component manufacturers held a series of meetings in Detroit in 1951. From those meetings (since referred to as the *Joint Industry Conference*, or *JIC*), a set of standards, fluid power symbols, and specifications that have become widely accepted and used throughout industry was evolved. The symbols, in particular, have equipped the fluid power designer and user with a common written language that transcends design variations, trade names, and even the normal language barriers between nations.

By 1954, the fluid power component manufacturers accepted this obvious challenge and formed the *National Fluid Power Association*, or *NFPA*, for the purpose of further strengthening the professional stature and service value of the fluid power industry. The development of standards for the fluid power industry and fluid power technology was a foremost objective of the *NFPA* at the time of its establishment—and this area is the most prominent single area of activity in the association today.

NFPA is an association of manufacturers of fluid power systems and components with a membership of well over one hundred companies throughout the United States. In addition to its interests in standardization, the association provides its membership with a variety of marketing, statistical, management, public relations, and educational services. In all these areas it represents the fluid power industry of the United States to other industries, governmental agencies, and the general public.

Until 1960, the development of fluid power standards was also a primary interest and purpose of the *Joint Industry Conference* (*JIC*), sponsored primarily by the automotive industry, but participated in by other consumers, manufacturers of fluid power equipment, and general interests. *JIC* was responsible for developing the first generally accepted standards for fluid power symbols and drafting practices and for the widely used *JIC Hydraulic and Pneumatic Standards for Industrial Equipment.* In 1958, the *JIC* fluid power symbols were adopted by the *American Standards Association* as American standards.

In 1960, the automotive industry ceased sponsorship of the *Joint Industry Conference.* Recognizing the necessity for providing further continuity to the excellent work of *JIC*, the *National Fluid Power Association* proposed that the development of future fluid power standards become a joint activity of *NFPA* and the *American Standards Association* (*ASA*). At a general conference called by *ASA* on September 28, 1961, *NFPA* was officially designated the sponsor of the newly organized *ASA* Sectional Committee, B93, Fluid Power Systems and Components, within the structure of *ASA*.

Under this administrative arrangement, *NFPA* is responsible for the development and review of recommended industry standards and for processing of fluid power industry standards through *ASA* Sectional Committee B93 for adoption as American standards. Current standards activity of *NFPA* includes not only the updating and revision of portions of the *JIC* recommendations but also the development of recommended standards in many additional areas.

One of the first and most notable efforts of the *NFPA* was to prepare and offer to the industry a "Glossary of Terms" which is felt by many to have dispelled much of the confusion that existed due to nonstandard nomenclature.

The *NFPA,* in turn, fostered the *Fluid Power Society,* a technical organization devoted to furthering the growing technology of fluid power, to fostering activities aimed at increasing the body of knowledge of fluid power, and to meeting the needs of fluid power—the exchange of ideas, techniques, and information, and the updating and upgrading of the members' knowledge of fluid power.

It was realized at the time of the formation of the *Fluid Power Society* that there was a need for an organization to serve all individuals interested in any phase of fluid power—research, development, design, application, installation, operation, maintenance, and education—and serving all fields of utilization—including industrial, aerospace, marine, mobile, materials handling, farm implements, etc.

The *Fluid Power Society* has made outstanding contributions to fluid power education in the past few years. It is a founding member of the *Council on Fluid Power Education* which is made up of representatives from six international educational and engineering organizations. It cosponsored, with the *National Fluid Power Association* and Wayne State University, the first summer institute on fluid power education for college teachers, and in 1965, the association secured a government contract for $234,000 to sponsor seven summer institutes for vocational and technical teachers.

The *Fluid Power Society* is a cosponsor of the *National Conference on Fluid Power*, a cosponsor of the *Fluid Power Seminars* conducted by the Milwaukee School of Engineering, and a cosponsor of seminars offered in cooperation with the *National Fluid Power Association*. It also cooperates with other societies on annual fluid power meetings, including the *American Society for Engineering Education*, and the *American Vocational Association*.

The foregoing is an indication of the high degree of maturity currently enjoyed by the fluid power industry, as well as the continuing efforts of a large number of extremely capable and experienced people in fostering a continuing growth.

REVIEW QUESTIONS

1. What is meant by the term "fluid power?"
2. What is the difference between fluid power and hydraulic power?
3. How did World War II expand the field of fluid power applications?
4. What is the outstanding contribution of the Joint Industry Conference (JIC) held in Detroit in 1951?
5. What are some of the outstanding contributions of the Fluid Power Society?

2

Power
or
Force
Components

The most basic component employed in a fluid power system is a force component—the cylinder. By definition, a *cylinder* is a linear motion device for converting fluid energy into mechanical energy, in which the thrust or force is proportional to the effective cross-sectional area.

CYLINDERS

Cylinders may be classified on a number of bases, and a given type of cylinder may fall into more than one classification. Some of these classifications are: single-acting or double-acting; air, oil, or water service; tie-rod construction, bolted-flange construction, retaining-ring construction, or welded construction; low, intermediate, high, or ultrahigh pressure; piston-type, ram-type, or diaphragm-type; etc.

Single-Acting

In a single-acting cylinder, the fluid force is applied in only one direction; it may produce either a "pushing" or a "pulling" force, depending on its construction. The return of the force member is accomplished by an internal or an external spring, by gravity, or by some outside force. Hydraulic lift cylinders, hydraulic jacks, and hydraulic wheel pullers are typical examples of the single-acting type of hydraulic cylinder. Single-acting air cylinders are usually of the spring-return type, and, like their hydraulic counterparts, are used where a working force is required in only one direction. They are more practical and are more commonly found in strokes of 3 inches, or less,

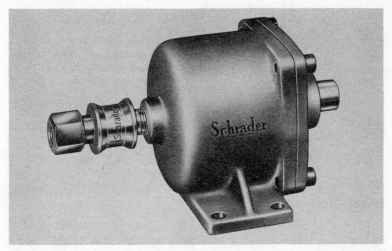

Courtesy A. Schrader's Son, Div. of Scovill Mfg. Co.

Fig. 2-1. A single-acting spring-return type of cylinder.

due to the spring-closure problem. Since the life of the return spring is somewhat limited, an appreciable savings in air consumption can be realized. The single-acting cylinder is usually the less expensive type because of its simple construction. The piston utilizes a seal that is required to seal in only one direction, and the rod seal is eliminated entirely, except in the pull-type cylinder. Also, only one fluid port or pipe tap is required (Fig. 2-1).

In the single-acting hydraulic cylinder, some requirements permit the elimination of the piston, utilizing the cross-sectional area of the rod for the fluid to work against. This is known as "ram-type," "ram-displacement," or "plunger-type" construction.

17

Another variation of the single-acting cylinder utilizes a flexible diaphragm instead of a piston. This diaphragm serves, then, as both a piston and a piston seal (Fig. 2-2). This type of cylinder is used as an air cylinder, and it is used to supply the braking force on most semitrailers on the road today.

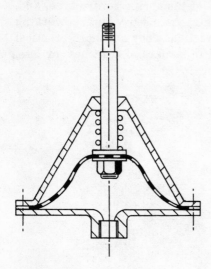

Fig. 2-2. A diaphragm-type single-acting cylinder in which the diaphragm serves as both a piston and a piston seal.

Double-Acting

In a double-acting cylinder, fluid force can be applied in either direction, creating alternate "push" and "pull" forces. There is considerable variation in the design of double-acting cylinders, but many component parts are common to all these cylinders: tube or barrel; bidirectional piston seal or seals; piston; piston rod (force member); rod seal; rod bearing; and cylinder covers or heads (Fig. 2-3).

Service Media

Variations in the component materials are dictated by the fluid media as well as by the operating conditions, such as ambient temperatures, severity of service, cost, and maintenance. Most cylinders that use air to supply the fluid force employ a corrosion-resistant material for the cylinder tube—brass being the most popular material. Plated steel is used occasionally, and even untreated steel can be used quite successfully with adequate air-line lubrication. The piston rod of the air cylinder is plated to guard against the possible corrosive action of water condensate entrained in the air supply. In more recent years, plating the cylinder rod has become standard with nearly all double-acting cylinders because of the greater wearing qualities. The rod bearing is usually made of high-grade bearing bronze or cast iron, either material presenting a suitable bearing surface for steel or plated rods. Piston seals are normally of the cup-type, "leathers," or "O"

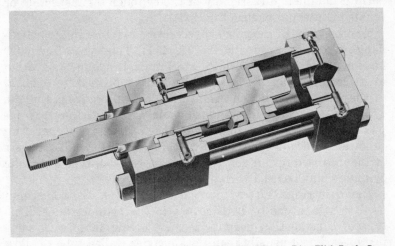

Courtesy Miller Fluid Power Div., Flick-Reedy Corp.

Fig. 2-3. Cutaway of a double-acting hydraulic cylinder.

rings, and they are made of synthetic rubber compounds, such as Buna N or neoprene, for air and water service. The automotive-type cast iron or metal rings are most commonly used in hydraulic service. The metal rings permit a slight by-pass of fluid, however; in some applications where this cannot be tolerated, such as for a holding action on a press circuit, composition cup-type or "block-vee" packings are used. If a system is to be charged with a hydraulic fluid other than a standard petroleum-base fluid, special attention is required in matching the seal materials with the characteristics of the special fluid. Incompatibility of these two items can result in excessive seal expansion, shrinkage, or complete deterioration of the sealing material, thus leading to contamination of the entire system and failure of the cylinder to function. If water is to be the fluid medium, stainless steel is usually the advisable material for component parts, particularly for piston rods.

External Construction

The most common method of holding a cylinder assembly together is with "tie rods" or "tie bolts." These tie rods are usually prestressed in the assembly of the cylinder in order to anticipate any stretching action that may occur as they absorb the fluid force within the cylinder. Removal of the tie-rod nuts permits complete disassembly of the cylinder for inspection or repair of internal parts (Fig. 2-3).

Another type of assembly construction is found in the bolted-flange or "mill-type" cylinder (Fig. 2-4). This type of cylinder has long been popular with the steel mills, hence the derivation of its common name. Disassembly is accomplished by removal of the flange bolts which are of unit length, regardless of the cylinder stroke. Since standard bolts are used, they are replaced easily if they are damaged in the rather severe operating conditions encountered in the steel mills. The mill-type air cylinder is used for air service up to 250 *psi*. Mill-type hydraulic cylinders may be used with pressures to 3000 *psi*.

Retainer rings, either internal or external, are sometimes used to attach one or both covers to the cylinder tube. This type of construction permits a space-saving feature in some instances, but it usually requires a heavier walled tube to allow

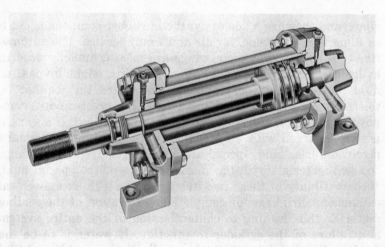

Courtesy Logansport Machine Co., Inc.

Fig. 2-4. Cutaway of a bolted-flange or mill-type cylinder.

for the grooving that is necessary to receive the retainer rings. The linear force exerted by the internal fluid pressure must also be absorbed by the tube.

Welded construction is usually encountered in cylinders that are commonly referred to as agricultural, farm-type, or mobile-equipment cylinders. In these cylinders the blind-end cover is welded, brazed, or silver-soldered to the tube, and no provision is made for disassembly from that end. This type of cylinder is usually mass produced with a specified bore, stroke, and mounting, and it is the least expensive cylinder on the market. Considerable savings in cost is realized at the expense of the flexibility and adaptability normally required in industrial applications.

One of the simplest, yet most misunderstood, features found in a double-acting cylinder is the cushion, which is an optional feature. A cushion is a device that is built into a cylinder to restrict the flow of fluid to the outlet port, thereby arresting, retarding, or decelerating the motion of the piston rod. This flow restriction is accomplished by means of a rod collar on the rod end of the piston entering a mating recess in the flow path through the cylinder cover. The same action is accomplished on the blind end of the piston by either a collar or an internal extension of the piston rod beyond the piston. The size or diameter of the cushion nose is not significant if it fits the cushion well closely enough to shut off the normal flow of fluid that exhausts through the cylinder port. The exhausting fluid is then diverted through a needled orifice to the cylinder port. On reversing the direction of the cylinder stroke, fluid is delivered to the piston area by by-passing the needled orifice through a check valve, thus eliminating any retarding action as it emerges from the cushion (Fig. 2-3). Some variations are found in cushion design, but this is the fundamental principle of the cushion, with the retarding action being affected by the effective area of the piston.

Another basic point of confusion with cylinders is probably due to improper choices of nomenclature by the fluid power industry in its infancy. This confusion crops up from time to time in the discussion of "rotating" and "nonrotating" cylinders. A "rotating cylinder" is specifically designed to rotate in its entirety (except for the distributor). The cylinder attached to the lathe spindle for controlling the jaws of a rotating chuck is an example of a rotating cylinder (Fig. 2-5). A "nonrotating cylinder" is designed for mounting in a relatively fixed, non-rotating position. The piston and/or force member of this type of cylinder can be rotated within the cylinder body unless internal or external provision is made to prevent its rotating. Then the cylinder becomes an "antirotating" or "guided-rod"

Fig. 2-5. A "rotating" type of cylinder; it can be attached to a lathe spindle to control the jaws of a rotating chuck.

cylinder. The amount of force delivered by the force member of a cylinder varies in direct proportion to the area of the piston that is exposed to fluid pressure and by the amount of fluid pressure applied.

Optional accessories are available for mounting or linking the cylinder to the work to be done. These optional mounting details are illustrated in Fig. 2-6.

FLUID MOTORS

Another important force component is the fluid motor, which is a rotary motion device for converting fluid energy to mechanical energy. The fluid motor may be of either the *fixed-*

MOUNTING STYLE

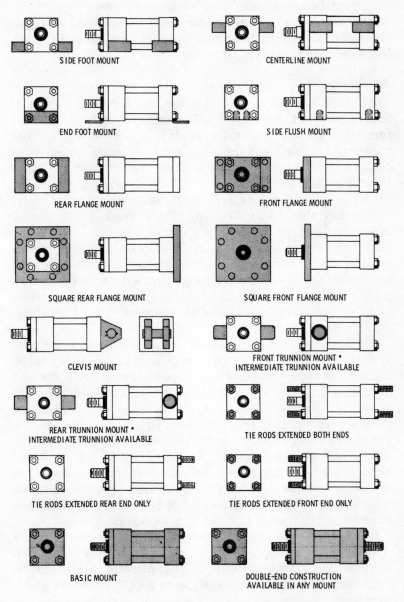

SIDE FOOT MOUNT

CENTERLINE MOUNT

END FOOT MOUNT

SIDE FLUSH MOUNT

REAR FLANGE MOUNT

FRONT FLANGE MOUNT

SQUARE REAR FLANGE MOUNT

SQUARE FRONT FLANGE MOUNT

CLEVIS MOUNT

FRONT TRUNNION MOUNT •
INTERMEDIATE TRUNNION AVAILABLE

REAR TRUNNION MOUNT •
INTERMEDIATE TRUNNION AVAILABLE

TIE RODS EXTENDED BOTH ENDS

TIE RODS EXTENDED REAR END ONLY

TIE RODS EXTENDED FRONT END ONLY

BASIC MOUNT

DOUBLE-END CONSTRUCTION
AVAILABLE IN ANY MOUNT

Courtesy Carter Controls, Inc.

Fig. 2-6. Optional mounting details for cylinders.

23

displacement type or the *variable-displacement* type. The variable-displacement design permits adjustment of the displacement per revolution, which cannot be done in the fixed-displacement motor. Fluid motors may be classified as either air motors or hydraulic motors, and each possesses characteristics peculiar to its type of motor.

Air Motors

Although the efficiency of the air motor falls far short of that of the electric motor, it offers some flexibilities and features that are not practical with electric motors. Applications requiring intermittent motion, extreme speed ranges, or lengthy stalls under load lend themselves readily to these favorable characteristics of air motors. Operations near volatile fluids or explosive hazards also tend to make the air motor highly desirable. In applications where speeds below the efficient range of air motors are required, some units are available with built-in speed-reducing gear trains, thereby adding considerably to their adaptability. Without notable exception, air motors are of the fixed-displacement type of construction, since the compressibility and the resulting volume variations of air do not make the variable-displacement type of construction practical.

Air Turbine—The most widely known air motor is referred to as the air turbine; it can be found in most dental offices. Its efficiency is apparent only at high speeds, and it produces very little torque at low speeds. Some of these air motors operate at speeds in excess of 500,000 *rpm*. These motors are also used in bone surgery, as burrs or bone drills.

Vane-Type—The most common air motor in terms of numbers being used throughout all industries is the vane-type motor. This motor has similar low-torque characteristics at low speeds, and is not capable of the extremely high speeds of the turbine. At the intermediate speed range of 1000 to 5000 *rpm*, however, it has proved to be quite a workhorse.

Piston-Type—The piston-type air motor is the most efficient of the various air motor designs, although it is, with few exceptions, the most expensive. It is capable of producing dependable torques at much lower speeds than either of the aforementioned designs, and its efficiency permits the delivery of much greater forces at a practical cost.

24

Hydraulic Motors

The hydraulic motor bears many of the characteristics of air motors, but it more nearly resembles the hydraulic pump in both construction and appearance. Hydraulic motors are capable of much higher torques, but they are more limited in top speed when compared with the air motor. These motors are capable of the same speed variations, stall characteristics, and intermittency; they are, in addition, capable of delivering dependable torques at lower *rpm*. They tend to become undependable at speeds below 50 to 300 *rpm*, depending on the specific design of the motor. Typical torque curves at various speeds are shown in Fig. 2-7 and Fig. 2-8.

Since the construction and design of hydraulic motors nearly duplicates that of hydraulic pumps, these items are discussed later in this text (see Chapter 6). Therefore, the various types of hydraulic pumps are merely mentioned here.

Gear-Type—The most common type of hydraulic motor is the spur-gear type. Although it is not the most efficient hydraulic motor, its low cost and simplicity have made it practical for many applications that do not warrant the sophistication of a more complicated and complex design. The torque and speed characteristics of a typical gear-type motor are shown in Fig. 2-7. The gear-type hydraulic motor can be run in either direction on the same installation with the use of an external drain to the sump. Generally speaking, a unidirectional hydraulic motor can be drained internally to the exhaust side of the motor element.

Vane-Type—The vane-type hydraulic motor is slightly more expensive and slightly more efficient than the gear-type motor. Although the gear-type motor is basically a fixed-displacement design, the vane-type motor sometimes borrows from its pump counterpart the variable-displacement feature that may be desirable in some more sophisticated systems. Torque and speed characteristics of a typical vane-type hydraulic motor are shown in Fig. 2-8. Most vane-type motors are unidirectional, although some designs permit the reversal of performance direction by making internal changes.

Piston-Type—This most efficient type of hydraulic motor is also the most expensive and the most sophisticated, although the piston-type motor covers a considerable range of price, de-

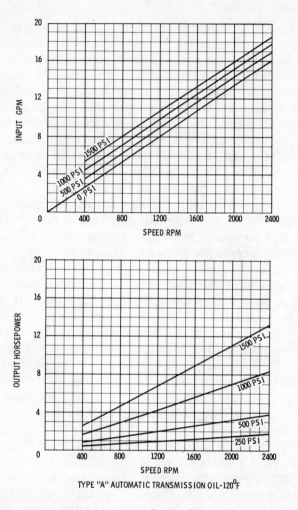

Fig. 2-7. Typical performance curve for a gear-type hydraulic motor.

pending on the features and refinements desired. It offers the widest range of sizes, torques, speeds, and horsepower of any units in the industry. The variable-displacement feature is also available in this type of motor. The piston-type motor usually demands more sophistication in the entire circuit, particularly in the area of filtration, due to the inherent low tolerance of

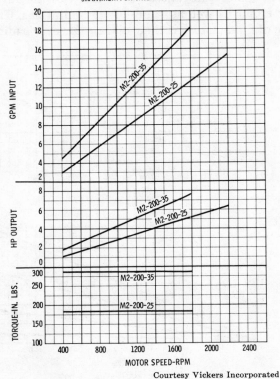

TYPICAL PERFORMANCE CURVES
SERIES M2-200 VANE MOTORS

OIL TEMPERATURE - 120°F. - OIL VISCOSITY 150 S.S.U. @ 100°F.
ALL CURVES SHOW CHARACTERISTICS AT 1000 PSI INLET PRESSURE
(MAXIMUM FOR INTERMITTENT SERVICE)

Courtesy Vickers Incorporated

Fig. 2-8. Performance curves for Series M2-200 vane-type hydraulic motor, showing torque and speed characteristics.

dirt and foreign materials in the fluid system. Most of these motors can be used as bidirectional units (see Fig. 2-9 for torque and speed characteristics of a typical piston-type motor).

Gerotor-Type—Most fluid power classification listings indicate that motors, as well as pumps, fall into the three categories—gear, vane, and piston types. Some persons in the industry, however, believe that the gerotor-type unit does not fit accurately in any of the three categories, although it is often referred to as a gear-type unit. In appearance it resembles the internal-gear design, but it more nearly matches the characteristics of the vane-type motor in performance. A rather unique variation of this unit provides for a speed reduction as an integral part of the internal design of the working element.

Hydraulic motors, in general, offer many of the advantages of the air motor as well as many of its limitations. The chief advantage of fluid motors is their disdain for overloading, even

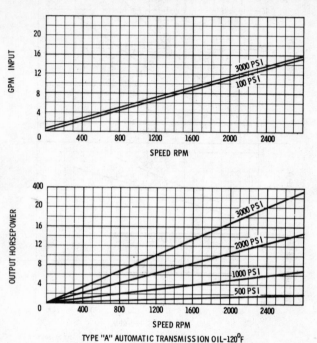

TYPE "A" AUTOMATIC TRANSMISSION OIL-120°F

Courtesy Webster Electric Co.

Fig. 2-9. Typical performance curves for a piston-type hydraulic motor.

to the point of complete and prolonged stalls. Their comparative safety when used in hazardous locations has led to their use in driving hydraulic pumps on installations so hazardous that the use of electric current is prohibited entirely. This type of installation would win no prizes for overall efficiency, but its value in this type of application is quite evident.

Torque Generator

Many applications require a type of torque that is slightly different from that delivered by a fluid motor. The need for

28

rotary motion or force through an arc that is less than a complete revolution resulted in the development of the "torque generator." This unit is bidirectional, possessing characteristics similar to those of a cylinder. It differs from the cylinder in that it delivers its force as rotary motion.

The vane-type torque generator with the design limitation of a limited degree of arc is one of the early types of torque generator. It is a fixed-displacement type of torque generator; its delivered torque is determined by the area of the vane, by the mean distance from the vane center point to the shaft center point, and by the fluid pressure that is applied (Fig. 2-10).

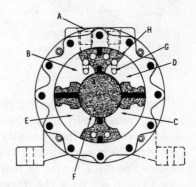

Fig. 2-10. Diagram of a vane-type torque generator.

Courtesy Houdaille Industries, Inc.

When high-pressure fluid enters the port A connected to the chamber B, it causes this chamber and the chamber C, which is connected by internal porting, to increase in volume. The other chambers D and E connected to the discharge port reduce in volume. This rotates the wing shaft F in a counterclockwise direction. Snubbing occurs at the ends of angular travel as the rotating wing shaft vane closes off the discharge port G and traps a small amount of fluid in chambers D and E. Rotation in the opposite direction is obtained by reversing the hydraulic pressure. Full speed response from the snubbed position is obtained through a check valve H.

A variation of this principle is found in the cylinder-type device shown in Fig. 2-11. This unit employs a guided piston that moves in a linear direction over a spiral-ground rod, thereby imparting circular motion to the rod. A tendency toward back-lash may be encountered with this unit, but it provides the advantage of deceleration by means of optional internal cushions of the type normally built into a cylinder. Its angle of rotation is less limited, since it can be built to deliver in excess of a complete revolution.

Another variation is the cylinder-type unit which generates torque by means of a cylinder-driven gear-rack mechanism that passes over a gear attached to the output shaft. This unit is similar in performance to the cylinder-type unit described in the preceding paragraph.

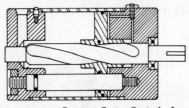

Fig. 2-11. Diagram of a cylinder-type torque generator.

Courtesy Carter Controls, Inc.

The power or force components described in this chapter are not necessarily all-inclusive, but they represent all but a small number of the specialty items currently available to the industry. New variations and new products are being developed within the fluid power industry at such a fantastic rate that any listing, such as the foregoing, is in danger of becoming obsolete while it is being published.

REVIEW QUESTIONS

1. Name three classifications of cylinders.
2. What is the chief difference between a single-acting cylinder and a double-acting cylinder.
3. What is the purpose of the cushion in a cylinder?
4. List three types of air motors.
5. List four types of hydraulic motors.

3

Linkages

The imaginative utilization of linkages is the key to the successful application of fluid power components. Careful thought should be given to the motion desired as well as to the required force at all points within that motion. If varying speeds within the motion are desirable, these variations often can be obtained by intelligent linkage design. Changing of lever angles, for example, offers an excellent method of obtaining acceleration and deceleration as well as either increasing or decreasing the forces in a moment arm. An unwise choice of linkage may, on the other hand, create unnecessary inefficiencies, wasted motions, larger than necessary force components, and maintenance problems that could otherwise be avoided.

The mechanical linkages to be employed in the attachment of the force component to the machine member or tool that is to perform work are of primary concern here. Attention is given later to fluid linkages, electrical linkages, and other types of linkages for control operation.

The standard cylinder-mounting options should become so familiar to the designer or cylinder user that he can recognize them by name as well as by their appearance and function (see Fig. 2-6). The foot-mounted, flange-mounted, side-flush mounted, and centerline-mounted options can all be used as rigid, nonflexing mountings. Their use presupposes absolutely no variation from simple straight-line motion. Proper alignment of the cylinder and the force member with the straight line of motion of the work unit is essential. Lack of attention to this detail can result in loss of efficiency, excessive wear on one side of the cylinder rod, shortened bearing life, and premature failure of the rod seal resulting from the abrading action of the scored rod passing through it.

The pivot- or clevis-mounted and the trunnion-mounted options are specifically designed to allow deviations from simple straight-line motion. On applications where proper alignment with the straight-line motion of the work unit is not possible, one of the latter mounting options should be considered, rather than a rigid type of mounting. The term "pivot mounting" is used to designate a swivel type of mounting, regardless of whether it is the single-eared or the double-eared appendage to the blind-end cover of the cylinder.

The use of a cylinder to move a lever represents the simplest and most common use of the pivot-mounted option (Fig. 3-1). Regardless of whether the first-, second-, or third-class lever is used, the cylinder, when attached to the lever with a hinge-type pin, undergoes a centerline movement as the lever moves through its arc. Application of levers may either multiply or reduce the effective force of the cylinder. The first-class lever may either increase or decrease the cylinder force, depending on the relative lengths of the lever arm on each side of the

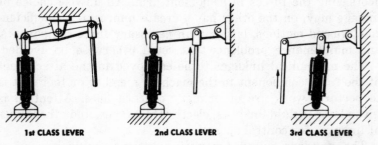

Fig. 3-1. The three classes of levers as linkages for nonrotating cylinders.

fulcrum or pivot axis. This is also true for the second-class lever; but, in the third-class lever, the resulting lever force is always less than the cylinder force. If the lever force is greater than the cylinder force, the cylinder stroke is greater than the lever stroke, and vice versa. In other words, *force times distance is equal to force times distance.* This principle can often be helpful in matching the cylinder bore and stroke to the work that is to be performed. The use of the pivot-mounted cylinder applied to the lever is one method of converting the straight-line motion of the cylinder to circular motion, imparting it to the pivot shaft of the lever in this instance. The effective force of this type of linkage is greatest when the centerline of the cylinder rod is perpendicular to the lever arm, and the effective force decreases as the angle described by the two members becomes more acute. At a constant cylinder speed, the rotational speed of the pivot shaft is greatest at this perpendicular condition, and the rotational speed decreases as the angle decreases, thus creating a natural accelerating and decelerating action of the pivot shaft. The pivot-shaft torque thus generated also varies in direct proportion to the speed.

Another common method of converting linear motion to rotary motion is the use of a cylinder to pass a gear-rack mechanism over a gear. In this application the rotational speed of the gear varies directly with the cylinder speed, and the torque remains constant. Acceleration and deceleration, in this instance, are accomplished either by cylinder cushions or by external flow controls. The amount of torque is determined by the cylinder force and the gear diameter. The degrees of arc result from the cylinder stroke and the gear diameter. A self-contained unit that utilizes the straight-line motion of a piston coupled with a chain and sprocket to produce rotary motion is shown in Fig. 3-2.

An unusually effective clamping linkage can be created by compounding the lever into a type of linkage that is commonly called a "scissors" (Fig. 3-3). In this type of linkage, the clamping pad moves in a straight line that is approximately perpendicular to the centerline of the cylinder rod. The motion characteristics of the clamping pad are ideal for clamping action. As the double lever arm approaches a straight line, the movement of the clamping pad decreases in speed and increases considerably in clamping force. By continuing the motion to

33

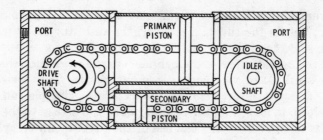

Courtesy Graham Engineering Company

Fig. 3-2. The use of the straight-line motion of a piston coupled with a chain and sprocket to produce rotary motion.

the point where the "toggle" becomes a straight line, an "on-center" condition is created, producing a holding force that is far in excess of the effective force of the cylinder itself. A simple screw-type adjustment of the fixed leg of the pivot permits regulation of this "on-center" force, as well as adapting it to the various sizes of the part being clamped.

By further compounding this linkage into a "double-scissors," tremendous final-squeeze and holding forces can be created, making this linkage ideal for use on holding presses. The holding force of the press platen in the "closed-and-locked" position provides the type of force that is required to hold the two halves of a pressurized cavity, such as that used in die-casting machines and in injection-type molding machines.

An effective type of linkage for compounding the stroke length of a cylinder is created by the use of a pulley and cable (Fig. 3-4). This type of linkage requires that the cylinder rod and bearing be of sufficient strength to withstand the distortion imparted to it by an unbalanced load. If this is not practical,

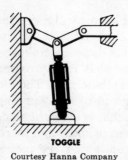

TOGGLE

Courtesy Hanna Company

Fig. 3-3. A "scissors-type" linkage for toggle application of the non-rotating type of cylinder.

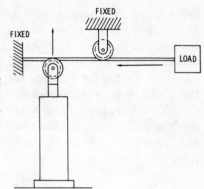

Fig. 3-4. The use of a cable and pulley to create an effective linkage for compounding the stroke length of a cylinder.

the path of the pulley must be supported, so that it can absorb or prevent any distorting influence from reaching the cylinder rod. Further compounding of the effective cylinder stroke can be created by the incorporation of additional pulleys. In each instance, the effective force of the cylinder is decreased by the amount of increase in the effective stroke.

Work requirements sometimes create a need for linear movement that may be in excess of the practical use of the cylinder as a force component. This situation sometimes arises when applying power to extra-long carriages. Using a rotary force component to produce this type of linear motion then becomes more practical. This type of linkage with the carriage attached to an endless chain passing over two sprockets, one of which is powered by a hydraulic motor, is shown in Fig. 3-5. A hydraulic braking circuit is often used with this type of linkage to decelerate heavy loads and to prevent mechanical shock damage resulting from too abrupt or too violent stopping. This type of circuit merely incorporates two relief valves, one for each side of the hydraulic motor circuit, and it is known as a braking and replenishing circuit.

Harmonic linear motion can be achieved quite efficiently by the use of the torque generator to produce straight-line movement (Fig. 3-6). With a constant rotational speed of the rotary actuator, the work load accelerates evenly in moving

Fig. 3-5. The use of a rotary force component to produce linear motion.

from point *A* to the center point, and it decelerates evenly
from the center position to point *B*. Maximum speed occurs at
the center position, as does maximum force. Care should be
taken in selecting the sizing of the torque generator to assure
adequate torque for starting the load at point *A*, as this point is
the position of minimum linear force in this type of linkage.
Continuous reciprocating harmonic motion can be achieved by
replacing the torque generator in Fig. 3-6 with a hydraulic
motor, continuing the rotation through an entire 360° of rotation.

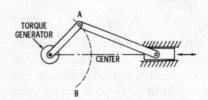

*Fig. 3-6. The use of a torque gener-
ator to produce straight-line or
linear movement.*

Another type of linkage that should be carefully considered
is the line of communication between the force component and
the control component. Probably, the most versatile of these
is the electrical linkage. By utilizing limit switches to originate
the control signals, the designer can simplify the problem of
mounting the control valves. Electrical wiring can more easily
encompass both distance and angularity, than can the fluid
plumbing lines, especially when appreciable flow rates are encountered. This, in turn, permits shortening the fluid lines,
reducing "pressure drops," and grouping or panel mounting
of the control components at a distance from the work areas of
the machine. Interlocks, safety circuits, and sequencing are
easily accomplished by the use of electrical linkages.

REVIEW QUESTIONS

1. Why are linkages important in the application of fluid power components?
2. What is meant by a "pivot-mounted" cylinder?
3. List four types of cylinder mountings.
4. How can a hydraulic braking circuit be used to prevent mechanical shock damage resulting from abrupt or violent stopping?
5. What is an advantage of an electrical linkage?

4

Control Components

In fluid power systems, the control valves can be divided into three categories: pressure controls, flow controls, and directional controls. Pressure controls are used to regulate the intensity of the pressure in various portions of the system. Flow controls are used to regulate the speed at which the medium (air, oil, or water) is allowed to flow, which, in turn, controls the speed of the cylinder pistons, the movements of the valve spools, rotation speeds of the shafts of fluid motors, and the actuation speeds of other devices. Directional controls are used to direct the fluid medium to the various passages in a system. There are many types of directional controls available—from simple shut-off valves (similar to those employed on sillcocks in the home) to the six- and eight-way control valves that are used to control automatic machinery.

Control valves are sized by their external openings or by the amount of fluid that can pass through them with minimum back-pressure. A control valve with external openings or pipe ports which are threaded for ½-inch pipe should be able to pass the same amount of fluid that a ½-inch pipe can pass normally.

It is generally agreed that the flow of hydraulic fluid should not exceed a rate of 15 ft. per second. However, there are instances where the oil velocity far exceeds this rate, and it may nearly double this rate. Excessive velocities of hydraulic fluid create heat in the system, and they contribute to control problems due to undesirable pressure drops.

Courtesy Versa Products Co., Inc.

Fig. 4-1. An air control valve with threaded pipe ports.

Most control valves are made with threaded pipe ports which are designated as *N.P.T.F.* (Fig. 4-1). Control valves often use subplate mountings or manifold-type mountings (Fig. 4-2). This permits replacement of the control valve without disturbing the piping.

Many of the larger valves employ flange-type connections (Fig. 4-3). These connections are generally used for ports larger than 2 inches, and they are used mostly for hydraulic service. Controls with straight pipe threads (*SAE*) are used mostly in hydraulics on military or mobile applications (Fig. 4-4).

The materials used in a control valve depend largely on the medium that passes through it, the operating pressure, and the ambient temperature. Pneumatic valves are made with alumi-

Fig. 4-2. Control valve with subplate mounting.

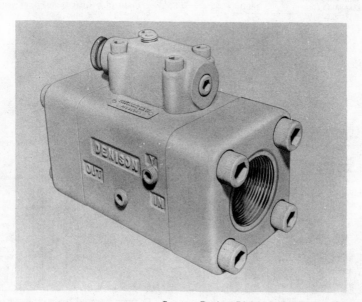

Fig. 4-3. A large hydraulic valve with flange connections, used
for high-pressure service.

num, brass, bronze, or cast-iron bodies, and the internal parts are made of brass, aluminum, stainless steel, or plated steels. Hydraulic valves are made with high-tensile cast iron, cast steel, or plate steel for body materials, and the alloy steels are used for the interior parts. Many of the interior parts are heat-treated to Rockwell C 55 or 60. Bronze or cast-iron alloys are used for the bodies of high-pressure water valves, and heat-treated steels or stainless steels are used for the interior parts. Care should be exercised in the selection of valves for high-pressure water systems, because high-velocity water erodes some types of materials. The resulting damage is called "wire-drawing effect," or "termite effect," and can render a valve completely inoperable in a short period of time.

Valve packings are made in various configurations and materials. Some of these configurations are cups, "O" rings, quad rings, "Vee" packings, "U" packings, etc. Some of the materials used are *Teflon*, *Viton*, Buna N, treated leather, asbestos, etc.

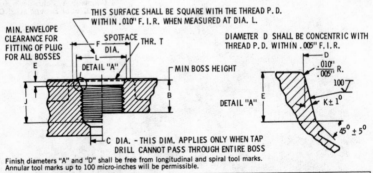

MEETS STANDARDS OF MS 16142 (SHIPS)

Finish diameters "A" and "D" shall be free from longitudinal and spiral tool marks. Annular tool marks up to 100 micro-inches will be permissible.

| tube outside diameter | Th'd. Size UNF-2B | STRAIGHT THREAD "T" | | | | B | C | D | E | F | J | K | L |
| | | Pitch Dia. | | Minor Dia. | | | | +.005 -.000 | +.015 -.000 | | | | |
		Min.	Max.	Min.	Max.	Min. Th'd. Depth	Min. Dia.	Dia.	Dia.	Dia.	Min.	±1°	Min. Dia.
⅛	⁵⁄₁₆-24	.2854	.2902	.267	.277	.390	.062	.358	.074	.672	.468	12°	.438
³⁄₁₆	⅜-24	.3479	.3528	.330	.340	.390	.125	.421	.074	.750	.468	12°	.500
¼	⁷⁄₁₆-20	.4050	.4104	.383	.395	.454	.172	.487	.093	.828	.547	12°	.563
⁵⁄₁₆	½-20	.4675	.4731	.446	.457	.454	.234	.550	.093	.906	.547	12°	.625
⅜	⁹⁄₁₆-18	.5264	.5323	.502	.515	.500	.297	.616	.097	.969	.609	12°	.688
½	¾-16	.7094	.7159	.682	.696	.562	.391	.811	.100	1.188	.688	15°	.875
⅝	⅞-14	.8286	.8356	.798	.814	.656	.484	.942	.100	1.344	.781	15°	1.000
¾	1¹⁄₁₆-12	1.0084	1.0158	.972	.990	.750	.609	1.148	.130	1.625	.906	15°	1.250
⅞	1³⁄₁₆-12	1.1334	1.1409	1.097	1.115	.750	.719	1.273	.130	1.765	.906	15°	1.375
1	1⁵⁄₁₆-12	1.2584	1.2659	1.222	1.240	.750	.844	1.398	.130	1.910	.906	15°	1.500
1¼	1⅝-12	1.5709	1.5785	1.535	1.553	.750	1.078	1.713	.132	2.270	.906	15°	1.875
1½	1⅞-12	1.8209	1.8287	1.785	1.803	.750	1.312	1.962	.132	2.560	.906	15°	2.125
2	2½-12	2.4459	2.4540	2.410	2.428	.750	1.781	2.587	.132	3.480	.906	15°	2.750

Courtesy Imperial Eastman Corporation

Fig. 4-4. Hydraulic control valves with straight pipe threads are commonly used on military and mobile applications.

PRESSURE CONTROLS

Pneumatic valves are generally designed for pressures up to 150 *psi*; hydraulic valves are designed for much higher pressures—1000, 2000, 3000, and 5000 *psi*, and even higher pressures. The various types of pneumatic and hydraulic pressure controls are:

Pneumatic	*Hydraulic*
pressure regulating	pressure relief
sequence	pressure reducing
safety	sequence
	counterbalance
	unloading

The air *pressure regulator* (Fig. 4-5) safeguards the pneumatic system, and the *pressure relief valve* (Fig. 4-6) safeguards the hydraulic system. Two types of air pressure regulators are the *relieving* and the *nonrelieving* types. With the relieving type of air pressure regulator (Fig. 4-7), downward regulating adjustments are possible without bleeding the line. Build-up in pressure in the reduced-pressure portion of the closed system is eliminated when the relieving type of regu-

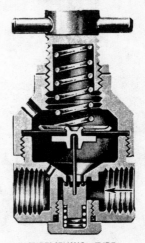

Fig. 4-5. An air pressure regulator.

NONRELIEVING TYPE
Courtesy Watts Regulator Company

41

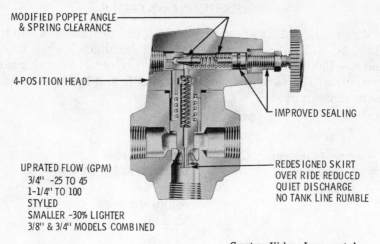

MODIFIED POPPET ANGLE & SPRING CLEARANCE

4-POSITION HEAD

IMPROVED SEALING

UPRATED FLOW (GPM)
3/4" -25 TO 45
1-1/4" TO 100
STYLED
SMALLER -30% LIGHTER
3/8" & 3/4" MODELS COMBINED

REDESIGNED SKIRT
OVER RIDE REDUCED
QUIET DISCHARGE
NO TANK LINE RUMBLE

Courtesy Vickers Incorporated

Fig. 4-6. Hydraulic relief valve.

lator is used. Although the upstream pressure (the pressure in the line between the source and the pressure regulator) may fluctuate considerably, the downstream pressure (the pressure between the regulator and the control valve) shows only slight

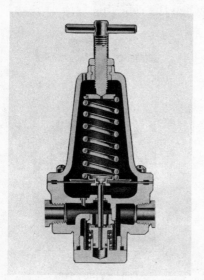

Fig. 4-7. Relieving type of air pressure regulator.

Courtesy Watts Regulator Company

variation, often less than 0.1 *psi*. The operating mechanism of the pressure regulator may be controlled by a diaphragm, a piston, or a bellows.

The *pressure relief valve* in a hydraulic system protects the pump and the means of driving the pump from overloading. It also protects the other components of the hydraulic system from excessive pressure. When the preset operating pressure is reached, the operating mechanism in the relief valve causes the oil to spill through to the exhaust port, thus relieving the pressure.

Relief valves are of several different types: the *direct-acting* type, with a spool or piston acting against a heavy spring; the *direct-operated pilot* type, which is pilot operated, with the piston acting against a small spring; and the *remote-actuated pilot* type, which is controlled through a remote valve. In the latter type of relief valve, the remote valve may be placed at a distance from the relief valve, and connected to the relief valve by piping.

Sequence valves are used for either air or oil and for the same purpose—to set up a sequence of operations. Quite often, a second four-way control valve can be eliminated by using one or two sequence valves. Sequence valves may be either the direct-acting type or the direct-operated pilot type of valve. The direct-operated pilot-type valve (Fig. 4-8) is used only for

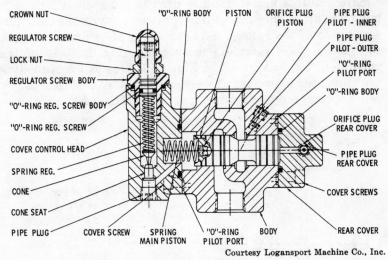

Courtesy Logansport Machine Co., Inc.

Fig. 4-8. A hydraulic sequence valve.

Fig. 4-9. An air sequence valve.

hydraulic service; the direct-acting valve (Fig. 4-9) may be used either for air or for low-pressure hydraulic service. By building the check valve into the sequence-valve body to provide free-flow return, piping and fittings can be eliminated at that point.

Safety valves are sometimes used in a pneumatic circuit; but, more often, they are used in conjunction with the compressor section of the system. A pneumatic type of sequence valve can be used as a safety valve by connecting the inlet of the valve to a "tee," as shown in Fig. 4-10. Less expensive valves are often used to prevent an overload condition, and they can be set to open at a predetermined pressure. These valves are simi-

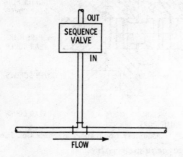

Fig. 4-10. An air sequence valve used as a safety valve.

lar in operating principle to the "pop-off" valve used on a hot-water tank in the home.

Pressure reducing valves are commonly used in hydraulic systems where more complicated requirements demand more than one operating pressure. Pressure reduction from the upstream side of the valve to the downstream side of the valve can be as much as 10 to 1. If the upstream side is 1000 *psi*, the downstream side may conceivably be reduced to 100 *psi*. Hydraulic pressure reducing valves are of two types: the *direct-acting valve* (Fig. 4-11); and the *direct-operated* pilot-type valve.

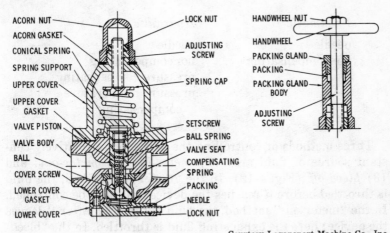

Courtesy Logansport Machine Co., Inc.

Fig. 4-11. A direct-acting hydraulic pressure reducing valve.

Hydraulic valves, such as the *counterbalance valve* and the *unloading valve* have fewer applications than the valves previously mentioned. The counterbalance valve is used to restrict a movement or to balance a load that is being held in position by a cylinder, motor, or actuator. The unloading valve is often used in hydraulic circuits to unload a pump or an accumulator. This valve is actuated from an external signal.

Pressure control valves that receive the operating signal from the upstream side are the sequence, safety, pressure relief, and counterbalance valves. The pressure regulating valves and the pressure reducing valves receive the operating signal from a downstream source. The source of the operating signal is significant primarily in identifying a valve in a circuit diagram, or in determining its specific function. This informaton can also be quite helpful in troubleshooting a malfunctioning system or component.

FLOW CONTROLS

Valves which control the amount of flow of the fluid are called *speed controls* in pneumatic systems and *flow controls* in hydraulic systems. The *noncompensating* type of control designed for pneumatic service is often used for low-pressure hydraulic service. The various types of flow controls are:

Pneumatic	*Hydraulic*
needle	needle
noncompensating	noncompensating
	pressure compensating
	pressure-temperature
	compensating

Three methods of controlling the flow from a relatively constant source of fluid are: (1) *meter-in*; (2) *meter-out*; and (3) *bleed-off* (Fig. 4-12). In the "meter-in" method, the fluid is throttled before it reaches the device that is to be controlled. In the "meter-out" method, the fluid is throttled after it leaves the device; here the exhausting fluid is throttled. In the "bleed-off" method, a portion of the hydraulic fluid is bled off before it reaches the device. The devices mentioned may be cylinders, fluid motors, actuators, or large controls.

Needle valves (Fig. 4-13) are used in both air and hydraulic systems to meter fluid. The design of the needle is important where fine metering is required. Dirty fluid can cause accuracy problems where fine metering must be accomplished.

Noncompensating-type flow controls are the most commonly used because of their low price and their availability. Although the noncompensating type cannot produce sufficient accuracy for extremely fine machine tool feeds, they perform satisfactorily in most installations. A speed-control valve that is used for both pneumatic service and low-pressure oil is shown in Fig. 4-14. A hydraulic flow-control valve used for high-pressure oil is shown in Fig. 4-15.

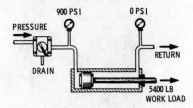

"METER-IN" CONTROL

Recommended for feeding grinder tables, welding machines, milling machines, and rotary hydraulic motor drives.

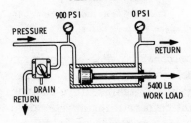

"BLEED-OFF" CONTROL

Recommended for reciprocating grinder tables, broaching machines, honing machines, rotary hydraulic motor drives.

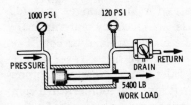

"METER-OUT" CONTROL

Recommended for drilling, reaming, boring, turning, threading, tapping, cut-off, and cold sawing machines.

Courtesy Vickers Incorporated

Fig. 4-12. Three methods of controlling hydraulic cylinder speeds are: meter-in (top); bleed-off (center); and meter-out (bottom).

Fig. 4-13. High-pressure needle valve for service at 5000 psi.

47

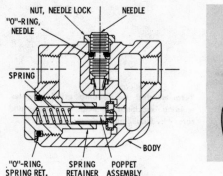

NUT, NEEDLE LOCK NEEDLE
"O"-RING, NEEDLE
SPRING
"O"-RING, SPRING RET. SPRING RETAINER POPPET ASSEMBLY
BODY

Courtesy Logansport Machine Co., Inc.

Fig. 4-14. A pneumatic speed-control valve.

Temperature- and pressure-compensated flow controls find considerable usage on machine tool applications where accurate feed rates are essential. The automatic temperature-compensating throttle provides a constant feed rate for any temperature setting, although temperature changes occur in the oil. The pressure-compensating device is a built-in pressure hydrostat that automatically compensates for any changes in loads. Compensation in each instance is achieved by automatically varying the orifice size to meet the changing load or condition (Fig. 4-16). This particular type of valve has a reverse free-flow from the outlet port to the inlet port. Pressure-compensated flow controls are available without the temperature compensator, and they are also built with an overload relief valve, as shown in Fig. 4-17. By using the overload relief valve, the only load that is imposed on the pump is the load that is needed

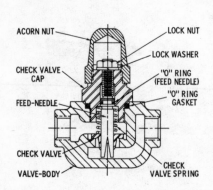

ACORN NUT LOCK NUT
CHECK VALVE CAP LOCK WASHER
"O" RING (FEED NEEDLE)
FEED-NEEDLE "O" RING GASKET
CHECK VALVE
VALVE-BODY CHECK VALVE SPRING

Courtesy Logansport Machine Co., Inc.

Fig. 4-15. A hydraulic flow-control valve.

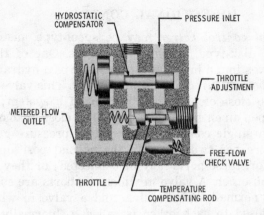

HYDROSTATIC COMPENSATOR

PRESSURE INLET

THROTTLE ADJUSTMENT

METERED FLOW OUTLET

FREE-FLOW CHECK VALVE

THROTTLE

TEMPERATURE COMPENSATING ROD

Fig. 4-16. Temperature- and pressure-compensated flow-control valve with check valve.

to overcome the work resistance. This reduces the input power and the heat losses in applications where the loads may vary considerably. By turning the dial on the face of the control to the "zero" setting, the pump can be unloaded completely. The pressure-compensated flow control assures accurate flow control despite the varying loads. These valves are available as either pipe port-in-body type or subplate mountings, with the latter being used more commonly.

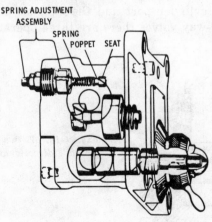

SPRING ADJUSTMENT ASSEMBLY

SPRING

POPPET   SEAT

Fig. 4-17. Flow-control and overload-relief valve.

DIRECTIONAL CONTROLS

Directional control valves may be spool-type, piston-type, poppet-type, disk-type, or plug-type valves. One of the most common valves found in either a pneumatic or a hydraulic system is the *two-way directional control valve.* This valve may be used: (1) to close or to open a portion of a system; (2) to close or to open an entire system; or (3) to close or to open the passage to a single component, such as a pressure gauge. A *two-way valve* has two ports. In the normal position of the valve actuator, these ports may be connected; or they may be closed to each other. A valve in which the ports are connected is called a "normally-open" valve, and a valve in which the ports are closed to each other is called a "normally-closed" valve (Fig. 4-18).

Three-way directional control valves have three port connections, and they may be "normally-open" or "normally-closed," when the valve actuator is in the normal or "at-rest" position. In a "normally-open" three-way valve (Fig. 4-19), the inlet is connected to the cylinder port, and the exhaust port is blocked. When the actuator is moved to the second position, the inlet port is blocked, and the cylinder port is connected to the exhaust port. In a "normally-closed" valve, the inlet port is blocked, and the cylinder port is connected to the exhaust port when the actuator is in the normal position. When the actuator is moved to the second position, the inlet port is connected to the cylinder port and the exhaust port is blocked. In some three-way valves there are three operating positions;

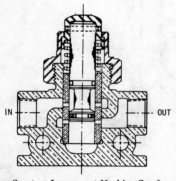

IN · · · · OUT

Fig. 4-18. A two-way "normally-closed" directional control valve.

Courtesy Logansport Machine Co., Inc.

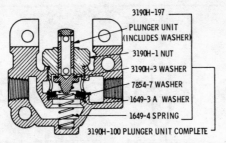

3190H-197 — PLUNGER UNIT (INCLUDES WASHER)

3190H-1 NUT

3190H-3 WASHER

7854-7 WASHER

1649-3 A WASHER

1649-4 SPRING

3190H-100 PLUNGER UNIT COMPLETE

Courtesy A. Schrader's Son, Div. of Scovill Mfg. Co.

Fig. 4-19. A "normally-open", three-way air control valve.

this type of valve is called a three-position, three-way valve. In the center operating position, all three ports can be blocked. This control is often used to actuate a single-acting cylinder (spring-return or gravity-return). The center position is a "hold" position, so that the piston of the cylinder can be positioned and stopped at any point in its range of travel. Three-way valves are employed to actuate single-acting cylinders, large control valves, fluid motors, fluid actuators, and regenerative systems. Two three-way valves can be used to actuate a double-acting cylinder.

Four-way directional control valves have four port connections—one inlet port, two cylinder ports, and one exhaust port. Some pneumatic four-way valves are built with two exhaust ports—one for each cylinder port. Speed controls are sometimes inserted in the exhaust ports. This arrangement can be quite satisfactory when used with an internally balanced valve. Hydraulic four-way control valves (Fig. 4-20) may be two-posi-

Fig. 4-20. Hydraulic four-way control valve.

Courtesy Logansport Machine Co., Inc.

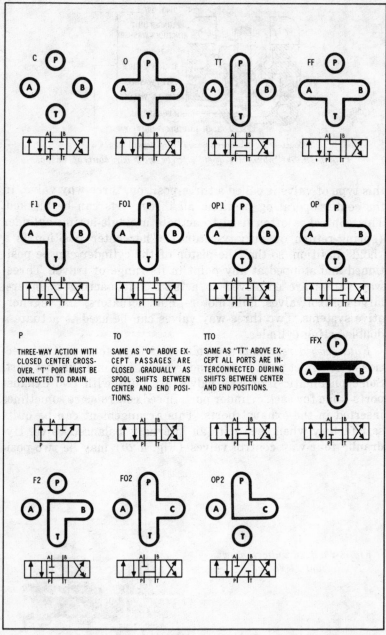

THREE-WAY ACTION WITH CLOSED CENTER CROSS-OVER. "T" PORT MUST BE CONNECTED TO DRAIN.

SAME AS "O" ABOVE EXCEPT PASSAGES ARE CLOSED GRADUALLY AS SPOOL SHIFTS BETWEEN CENTER AND END POSITIONS.

SAME AS "TT" ABOVE EXCEPT ALL PORTS ARE INTERCONNECTED DURING SHIFTS BETWEEN CENTER AND END POSITIONS.

Fig. 4-21. Hydraulic spool configurations.

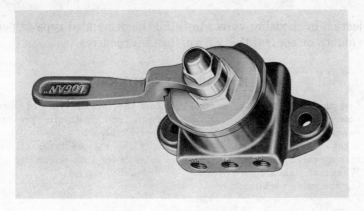

Courtesy Logansport Machine Co., Inc.

Fig. 4-22. Six-way air control valve.

tion or three-position valves. The *two-position four-way valve* has two positions for the actuator, and the *three-position four-way valve* has three positions for the actuator. The directional device (spools, pistons, etc.) in these valves may be spring-centered, spring-offset, or without springs. This is discussed in the following chapter which deals with types of valve operators.

Some of the spool configurations that are found in hydraulic valves are shown in Fig. 4-21. Pneumatic valves use many of the same configurations, except for those arrangements in which the pressure is exhausted in neutral position, thus permitting considerable waste of energy.

Four-way valves are utilized to actuate double-acting cylinders, fluid motors, fluid actuators, intensifiers, large control valves, etc. *Five-way control valves* are built with two inlet ports, two cylinder ports, and one exhaust port.

Specialty-type valves are found in directional controls such as the six- and eight-way directional control valves. A six-way directional control with one inlet port, four cylinder ports, and one exhaust port is shown in Fig. 4-22. Eight-way control valves are built with two inlet ports, two exhaust ports, and four cylinder ports, with an actuator of the "joy-stick" type. This type of valve can be used to control two cylinders at the same time.

A wide range of controls is now available. The designer and the maintenance personnel can avail themselves of quite a wide selection in choosing valves to fulfill the demanded type of performance or control that an application requires.

REVIEW QUESTIONS

1. List the three types of control valves that are used in fluid power systems.
2. What configurations are used in making valve packings?
3. What materials are used in making the valve packings?

4. List the various types of pneumatic and hydraulic pressure control valves?
5. List the various types of flow controls for both pneumatic and hydraulic systems.

5

Valve
Operators

In the preceding chapter the various controls that are used
in pneumatic and hydraulic systems were discussed. For these
controls to function, some means of operating them must be
provided. In most instances, pressure controls and flow controls utilize operators that are different from the operators
used by directional controls. In general, many types of operators are available as standard equipment for directional controls. The selection of a suitable valve operator is important,
since a poor choice may lead to considerable difficulties in
creating and maintaining the efficiencies and controllability
desired in a given system.

PRESSURE CONTROL VALVE OPERATORS

Pressure control operators are made in relatively few general types. Among these operators are the direct-acting screw,
the direct-acting cam roller, the offset cam roller, and the pilot.
Nearly all types of air and hydraulic pressure control valves

use a *screw-type operator* for setting the correct spring tension at which the valve is to function. The screw-type operator used on an air pressure regulator is shown in Fig. 5-1. As the screw is advanced, the downstream pressure is increased; as it is retracted, the downstream pressure is decreased.

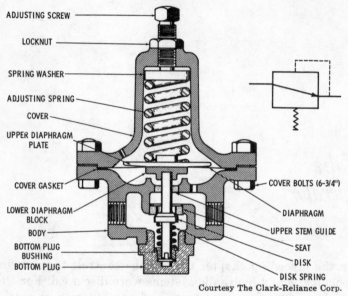

Courtesy The Clark-Reliance Corp.

Fig. 5-1. A diaphragm-type pressure regulator having a screw-type operator.

A sequence valve with a screw-type operator is shown in Fig. 5-2. As the screw is advanced, the tension on the spring is increased, thereby increasing the fluid pressure required to unseat the poppet and permit the compressed air to flow to the secondary circuit.

In a direct-acting spring-operated hydraulic relief valve (Fig. 5-3), the operating pressure of the system is increased, due to the spring tension placed on the spool, as the screw-type operator is advanced.

The *direct or offset cam roller type of operator* is employed more often on special application valves. For example, the use of this type of operator on a relief valve is advantageous if a considerable increase in pressure must occur at a given point

Fig. 5-2. A sequence valve with a
screw-type operator.

in the travel of the piston in a cylinder. At that point, a cam can be placed on the machine table or other moving member; at the correct position, the cam depresses the cam roller operator on the relief valve, causing the operating pressure to increase greatly.

Cam-type operators are also found on hydraulic relief valves used for testing applications where cams that have an extremely shallow angle are used. The cam roller is depressed gradually and pressure readings are recorded.

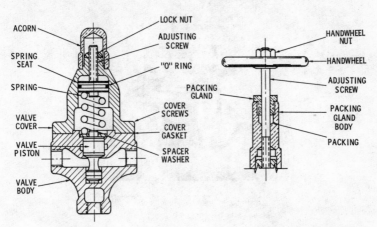

Fig. 5-3. Hydraulic relief valve with a screw-type operator.

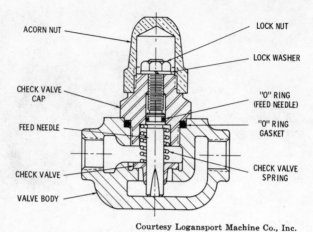

Courtesy Logansport Machine Co., Inc.

Fig. 5-4. Hydraulic flow control with a screw-type operator.

SPEED OR FLOW CONTROL VALVE OPERATORS

Speed or flow control valve operators, in nearly all instances, utilize some type of screw or threaded mechanism to open and to close the control orifice in the valve. The screw mechanism may be in the form of a needle with slots, as shown in Fig. 5-4,

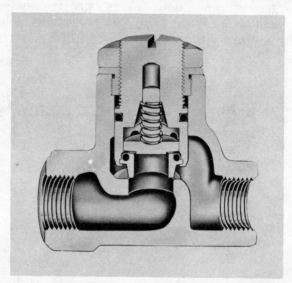

Courtesy A. Schrader's Son, Div. of Scovill Mfg. Co.

Fig. 5-5. Threaded mechanism used in a pneumatic speed control.

which is used in a hydraulic valve for pressures up to 3000 *psi*. After the correct flow is reached, the needle is locked in place with a lock nut. A threaded mechanism used in a pneumatic speed control valve is shown in Fig. 5-5. As the threaded mechanism is advanced, the orifice through which the metered air passes is reduced. The check arrangement permits a free-flow return of the air through the valve. The threaded mechanism is locked in place with a lock nut.

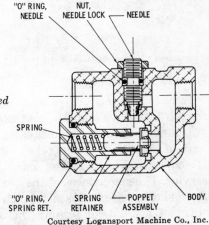

Fig. 5-6. Screw-type operator used in an air speed control valve.

Courtesy Logansport Machine Co., Inc.

A screw-type mechanism in the form of a needle is used in the air speed control valve shown in Fig. 5-6. This valve is also suitable for low-pressure oil. The needle is installed in the valve so that the major diameter cannot be backed out beyond the retaining pin, which is a safety feature. The screw or threaded mechanism may be equipped with a handwheel, a micrometer-type knob, a locking device, or some other type of mechanism for controlling it.

DIRECTIONAL CONTROL VALVE OPERATORS

Directional control valve operators may be classified in a number of different categories, and each category may consist of several types of operators. Some of these categories are manual, solenoid, mechanical, automatic-return, and pilot operators. Combinations of these types of operators are also available.

Fig. 5-7. Hand-type operator for a hydraulic directional control valve.

Courtesy Logansport Machine Co., Inc.

Manual Operators

In most instances, the manual type of operator is considered the most positive and the least expensive. A manual-type operator may be actuated by means of the hand, foot, or some other part of the body. A control designed for hand-type operation is shown in Fig. 5-7. The valve shown is used for hydraulic service. The ruggedness of the *hand-type operator* can be noted. A workman often uses a wrench or a piece of bar stock, instead of a hand, to actuate the operator, hence the need for built-in ruggedness.

A control designed for foot operation is shown in Fig. 5-8. The valve shown in the illustration is used for pneumatic service; a latch mechanism causes the valve spool to be held

Fig. 5-8. Foot-operated directional control valve that may be used for pneumatic service.

Courtesy Logansport Machine Co., Inc.

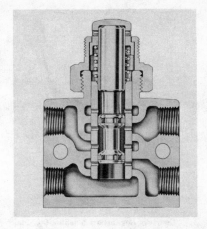

*Fig. 5-9. Spring-offset type of oper-
ator used for an air directional
control valve.*

Courtesy Logansport Machine Co., Inc.

in either of two positions—even though the foot is removed
from the valve operator.

Knee-type operators are sometimes utilized, especially on
air directional controls. These valves can be operated easily
when the worker is in a sitting position, thereby freeing the
worker's hands for work positioning, etc. If there is a possibility that a worker's hands may be endangered, the knee- or
foot-type operators should be eliminated, and hand-type operators should be used in a "no-tie-down" circuit.

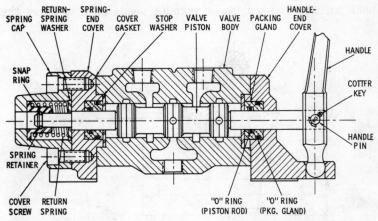

Courtesy Logansport Machine Co., Inc.

*Fig. 5-10. Spring-centered hand-type operator on a hydraulic directional
control valve.*

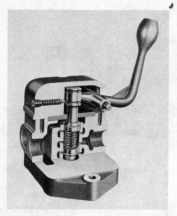

Fig. 5-11. Hand-type operator with detent on a pneumatic four-way control valve.

Hand-type operators may be of the spring-offset type (Fig. 5-9), spring-centered type (Fig. 10), detent-type (Fig. 5-11), or two-position (Fig. 5-12) without any friction stops.

When the *spring-offset type of operator* is used, the workman must keep his hand on the operator until he desires to change the direction of flow within the valve. When released, the operator automatically shifts back to its original position.

When the *spring-centered type of operator* is used, the workman must apply force to the operator handle in either outward position to prevent the handle returning to the neutral position. When an operator that uses a detent to find and to hold the spool position is used, the workman needs only to move the

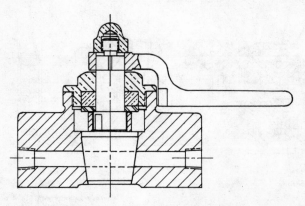

Fig. 5-12. Two-position, four-way directional control valve without friction stops.

handle until he feels the handle drop into the detent. The handle remains in place until the workman moves it to another position. Detents are used in two-position and in three-position control valves.

Sometimes a control valve that requires two valve operators may be necessary; one operator is used to shift the valve spool manually in one direction, and the other operator is used to

Fig. 5-13. Hydraulic four-way directional control valve with mechanical reversing mechanism.

Courtesy Logansport Machine Co., Inc.

reverse the valve spool by means of a solenoid or by some mechanical means. This arrangement permits the workman to move some distance from the directional control valve and perform another task while the fluid power equipment goes through its cycle. A hydraulic four-way directional control valve in which the spool is reversed by mechanical means is shown in Fig. 5-13.

Solenoid Operators

Solenoid operators consist of three general types: (1) the direct-acting solenoid; (2) the solenoid using a mechanical linkage; and (3) the solenoid pilot operators. The *direct-acting solenoid operator* is utilized on both air and hydraulic directional controls; in this type of control, the solenoid plunger acts directly against the end of the valve spool in order to shift it. An air directional control with two direct solenoid operators is shown in Fig. 5-14. The air directional control shown in the illustration does not function unless the valve covers are in place. This feature protects the solenoid from dirt, which reduces the possibilities of malfunction of the solenoids. Also, the

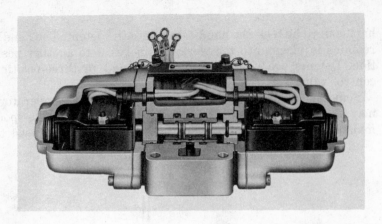

Fig. 5-14. Air directional control with two direct solenoid operators.

solenoid is protected from any moisture that may be collected in the exhaust of the valve by the "O" ring on the valve stem. Manual push pins are employed in conjunction with the solenoid operator, so that the spool of the valve can be shifted before the electric wiring is connected to the valve. This permits the system to be cycled and checked thoroughly before the electrical connections are made.

The inrush and holding current of solenoids employed on various sizes of hydraulic valves using direct solenoid operators is shown in Table 5-1. Large direct-acting solenoid operators cause considerable noise when they are energized, due to the weight of the solenoid plungers. The large direct-acting sole-

Table 5-1. Inrush and Holding Current of Solenoids Used on Hydraulic Valves (Volt-Amperes)

Valve size	60 cycle		50 cycle	
Ports	Inrush	Holding	Inrush	Holding
⅜"	1970	165	1650	150
¾"	5450	390	4450	325
1"	6900	510	5750	460
1½"	12600	715	10500	590
2"	31200	1760	37000	1460
$\text{Amperes} = \dfrac{\text{volt-amperes}}{\text{volts}}$				

noid operators are not generally employed on high-cycling applications, due to the severe impact.

Direct-acting solenoid operators are available in various voltages, such as 115 volt, 230 volt, etc., for alternating current; in most instances they are suitable for continuous duty. This means that the solenoid coil may be energized for an indefinite length of time. Solenoids of this type are also available for direct-current applications and are usually equipped with

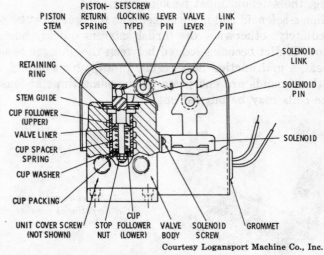

Courtesy Logansport Machine Co., Inc.

Fig. 5-15. Solenoid with mechanical linkage for operating the directional control valve.

a cut-out mechanism, often referred to as a "mouse trap." Direct-current solenoids normally are not recommended for continuous service.

A solenoid that uses a mechanical linkage is shown in Fig. 5-15. Note the mechanical advantage produced by the linkage. This permits the use of a smaller solenoid than can be used in a direct-acting solenoid operator, but a longer stroke is usually required.

Two-position directional control valves that use the direct-acting solenoid operator on one end of the valve and a spring-return operator on the other end are widely used for both pneumatic and hydraulic service. This eliminates one solenoid, which reduces the cost of the control valve. This combination is commonly used in the design of "fail-safe" circuits. A disadvantage is that the solenoid plunger works against the spring, and it must be kept energized in order to maintain the spool in position against the spring. Where the two direct-acting solenoid operators are used, except on three-position spring-centered valves, the solenoid needs only to be energized momentarily in order to shift the valve spool. A solenoid operator which uses the mechanical linkage can also use a spring-return operator. Here again, when the spool is working against the spring, the solenoid must be kept energized.

When a solenoid coil is energized, the plunger must be seated immediately; otherwise, the inrush current quickly burns out the coil. If dirt becomes lodged between the plunger head and the seat, a malfunction may result. In a double solenoid valve, if both solenoids are energized at the same time, at least one of the coils may be burned out.

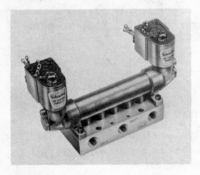

Fig. 5-16. A solenoid pilot operator for a directional control valve.

Courtesy A. Schrader's Son,
Div. of Scovill Mfg. Co.

Solenoids with plug-in connections are available (see Fig. 5-14), so that the solenoid can be replaced without disturbing the electric wiring. Indicator lights are often used in conjunction with the solenoids to indicate which solenoid is energized.

Solenoid pilot operators are common, and, in most instances, they are quite inexpensive. They are compact and require only a small space. The inrush and holding current are quite low, for example, 0.290 amperes inrush current and 0.210 amperes holding current for 115-volt, 60-cycle current. These operators are available for either alternating current (a-c) or direct current (d-c).

Solenoid pilot operators are available as a complete two-way or three-way valve (Fig. 5-16) used to control pilot-operated valves; or as a subassembly. Solenoid pilot operators are available with explosion-proof housings for use in hazardous locations.

Mechanical Operators

Mechanical operators on directional control valves play an important role on automatic equipment. The most commonly used mechanical operators are the direct-acting cam-roller type, the toggle lever type, the mechanical lever type with roller, the pin type, and the mechanical link type.

In the *direct-acting cam-roller type of operator*, more force is usually required to depress the roller, since it is acting against a spring. The angle on the cam should not be too abrupt, to avoid placing an excessive side load against the cam roller and the bearing in the valve cover.

The direct-acting cam-roller type of operator is found on some of the smaller directional control valves, but it is more commonly used on the larger more rugged valves for both pneumatic and hydraulic service. This type of operator requires a rather short stroke to complete an actuation. The cam roller should not be overstroked, although most of these valves provide for some overtravel. The cam is usually attached either to a machine table or to the piston rod of a cylinder. If it is attached to the piston rod of a cylinder, the rod should be supported near the contact point to eliminate deflection of the piston rod. Rotary cams are often used to actuate the cam roller.

The *toggle lever type of operator* requires only slight effort to actuate it. An inexpensive trip mechanism can be employed. This may be attached to a machine slide, to a feed mechanism, to a piston rod of a cylinder, or to some other moving mechanism. A workpiece moving down a conveyor can be used to trip the toggle mechanism.

The *mechanical lever type of operator* is similar in operation to the direct-acting cam operator, except that the line of action is offset and a mechanical advantage is created. This reduces the effort required to actuate the valve, although it does require a longer stroke to actuate the spool or flow director.

Return-type operators for directional controls can be of the spring type. The spring returns the spool or flow director to the neutral position, as in a three-position directional control valve; or it may return the spool or flow director to the end opposite the spring, as in a two-position directional control valve. A valve in which the spool is returned to the neutral position when the spring is released is shown in Fig. 5-10. The spring-return type of operator is used in conjunction with manual, solenoid, mechanical, and pilot types of operators.

Pilot Operators

Pilot types of operators are of the direct, bleed, or differential types, and they are found on valves where high cycling, safety interlocks, and automatic sequencing are required. A direct pilot operator used on a four-way hydraulic control valve is shown in Fig. 5-17. The medium which actuates the pilot operator is hydraulic fluid. To provide for better control of the spool as it shifts, chokes are often employed between the pilot operator and the spool. If two direct pilot operators are employed (one at each end of the spool assembly), two chokes are usually used. Adjustable orifices in these chokes are controlled by a needle, and, in some instances, one choke may be set differently from the other choke, so that the spool shifts faster in one direction of travel.

Although most hydraulic directional control valves which use direct pilot operators make use of hydraulic fluid as the medium for shifting the main valve spool, more applications are now being found for compressed air as the shifting medium. There are several advantages in using compressed air as the medium. The controls which direct the fluid to the direct pilot operators are less expensive, are more compact, and are

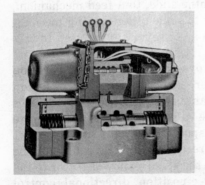

Fig. 5-17. Pilot-operated hydraulic four-way directional control valve.

Courtesy Logansport Machine Co., Inc.

manufactured in greater variety. Compressed air provides for faster spool shifting. Interlocks can be set up between a pneumatic system and a hydraulic system, permitting the use of air pressure for clamping and the use of hydraulic pressure for a heavy work cycle. Also, the necessary piping between the directional control and the operator is less expensive than when an all-hydraulic system is used.

Air-actuated direct pilot operators are now manufactured in which the diameter of the operator is sufficient for permitting an air pressure of three to five *psi* to shift the spool in the directional control valve, although the valve itself is subjected to an oil pressure of 3000 *psi*.

Compressed air is usually the operating medium for the direct pilot operators that are used on pneumatic directional control valves. In the differential-pressure type of operator (Fig. 5-18), pressure is placed on both ends of the spool operating mechanism, but the larger area of one mechanism causes the spool to travel toward the end with the smaller area. When the pressure is released from the larger area, the spool shifts to that end of the valve. The pressure differential action is similar to that of a spring, but it has the advantage of eliminating spring breakage caused by fatigue.

Bleed-type pilot operators are most often utilized to control a pneumatic directional control valve, as shown in Fig. 5-19. The bleed-type pilot operators are pressurized at all times

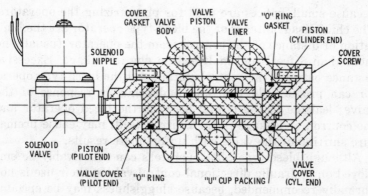

Courtesy Logansport Machine Co., Inc.

Fig. 5-18. Differential-pressure type of operator on a pneumatic four-way directional control valve.

69

through internal passages in the body of the valve. Whenever the pressure is released from either pilot chamber, an unbalanced condition exists, and the spool is shifted toward the pilot chamber where the air pressure has been released. The advantages of the bleed-type pilot operators are: external piping is eliminated; controls can be attached directly to the pilot operators; controls are inexpensive (only two-way controls are required); and high cycling is possible without excessive shock,

Fig. 5-19. Bleed-type operators for a four-way directional control valve for air service.

Courtesy Logansport Machine Co., Inc.

because small orifices are used for pressurizing the operators. The chief disadvantages of the bleed-type operator are the limitation of distance of the control from the operator (usually no more than 8 feet) and malfunction due to leakage. Excessive distance between the control station and the bleed-type operator can produce sluggish and undependable response of the valve; leakage in the piping between the bleed operator and the control, or leakage in the control itself, may cause premature shifting of the valve with unfortunate results.

Although bleed-type pilot operators can conceivably be employed on hydraulic directional control valves, their use is not normally recommended, because sluggishness may be encountered in shifting of the spool, and seal problems may occur within the valve.

REVIEW QUESTIONS

1. What is the purpose of the valve operator?
2. List three types of pressure control valve operators.
3. What type of operator is used for nearly all speed or flow control valves?
4. List four types of directional control valves.
5. What applications are most suitable for pilot operator directional control valves?

6

Pumps and Compressors

The utilization of hydraulic fluid power is based on Pascal's principle stating that "pressure applied to an enclosed gas or liquid is transmitted equally and undiminished in all directions." Energy in the form of a pressurized enclosed fluid offers one of the most versatile means of controlling motion and transmitting power. The enclosed fluid assumes the shape of any body that resists its thrust; it is positive, yet flexible, and its power-weight ratio is quite favorable, permitting the transmission of maximum power with comparatively small and flexible components.

PUMPS

Fluid, under pressure, is generated by pumps of many and varied designs. By definition, a pump is a device which converts mechanical energy into fluid energy. The characteristics of the pressurized fluid may vary considerably between one application requirement and another. To meet this wide range of requirements, the fluid power industry offers a rather impressive range of pumps, varying not only in design but also in capacity and adaptability—from capacities of a small number of cubic inches per minute to hundreds of gallons per minute; from extremely low pressures to high pressures of 30,000 *psi*, either constant-pressure or intermittent-pressure types; and covering an ever-increasing range of operating and fluid temperatures.

Centrifugal Pumps

The centrifugal pump is a relatively inexpensive pump that is capable of very limited pressures. It is a nonpositive-displacement type of pump, with an effective volumetric delivery

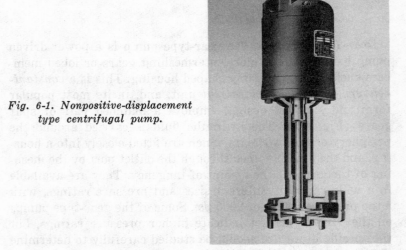

Fig. 6-1. Nonpositive-displacement type centrifugal pump.

Courtesy Brown & Sharpe Mfg. Co.

rate that drops off quite rapidly as pressure resistance increases in the discharge chamber. These pumps are most popular as fluid transfer pumps, for supercharging high-pressure pumps, and for prefilling of cylinders. Although their high "slip" rate renders them undesirable for use as a power source, this characteristic is ideal for supercharging and for fluid transfer. Relief or safety valves are not needed, since the nonpositive-displacement feature permits the pump to "slip" its entire capacity when the downstream volume demand has been met (Fig. 6-1).

Rotary Pumps

The most popular type of pump found in machine tool, automotive, aircraft, transmission, press, and mobile equipment application is the rotary design of pump, which is used primarily in creating fluid power sources in hydraulic systems.

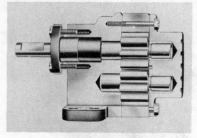

Fig. 6-2. A constant-delivery positive-displacement gear-type pump.

Gear-Type Pumps—The gear-type pump is a power-driven pump having two or more intermeshing gears or lobed members enclosed in a suitably shaped housing. This is a *constant-delivery, positive-displacement* unit, and, in its most popular form and simplest design, employs a matched pair of spur gears (Fig. 6-2). The hydraulic fluid is carried around the periphery of the two gears which are fitted closely into a housing, and the fluid is forced through the outlet port by the meshing of the gears at their point of tangency. They are available in a wide range of different sizes and pressure ratings, with a top pressure rating of 2000 *psi*. Some of the gear-type pumps on the current market indicate higher pressure ratings, but the specific literature should be studied carefully to determine the acceptable conditions for these pressures.

Fig. 6-3. Sectional view of a rotary gear-type pump with helical gears.

74

Gear-type pumps are built from a variety of materials ranging from cast-iron bodies with cut gears for the lower pressures, to *Meehanite* or steel bodies and ground gears for the higher pressures. These pumps are very practical units, but the comparatively high noise level can be objectionable when used for some applications. To lower the noise level and to dampen pulsations, a number of deviations have been made from the spur-gear. Two of these deviations are the helical gear shown in Fig. 6-3, and the herringbone gear shown in Fig. 6-4.

Gear-type pumps, in general, are relatively low in mechanical efficiency because of hydraulic unbalance, which creates the problem of high bearing loads at the higher pressures. Although they are most popular in applications where moderate pressures, constant-volume, and the higher viscosity fluids are to be handled, their lower initial cost sometimes projects them into more sophisticated applications.

This type of pump, because of its compactness, lends itself to tandem or double-pump assemblies. This combination presents a convenient method for producing, within a single power

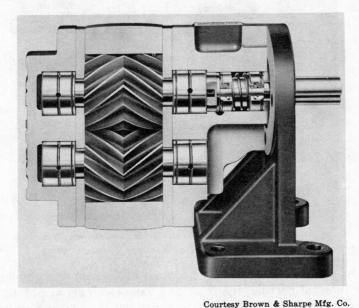

Courtesy Brown & Sharpe Mfg. Co.

Fig. 6-4. Sectional view of a rotary gear-type pump with herringbone gears.

unit, the high-volume low-pressure and the low-volume high-pressure circuits, the dual-pressure circuits, or the matched flows.

Vane-Type Pumps—The vane-type pump may be of either the fixed-delivery type or the variable-delivery type. The former type of pump is a power-driven pump having constant volume, with multiple vanes within a supporting rotor, encased in a cam ring (Fig. 6-5). In each rotor slot, a flat, rectangular vane (or vanes) is free to slide radially. Centrifugal force (sometimes assisted by a spring) drives the vanes outward, so that they follow the contour of the housing of the hardened cam ring within the housing. The vanes serve as dividers between the inlet and outlet ports, drawing the liquid inward at the suction side as the vanes extend and forcing the liquid outward at the outlet port as the cam ring pushes the vane inward; the volume between the vanes is thereby reduced. This unit then becomes a positive-displacement, constant-flow fluid pressure generator.

Courtesy Denison Division, Abex Corporation

Fig. 6-5. Cutaway view of a vane-type hydraulic pump.

By utilizing an oval-shaped contour of the cam ring and double internal porting, the rotor and vane assembly are brought into balance; this reduces side thrust on these members and permits higher output pressures without excessive bearing

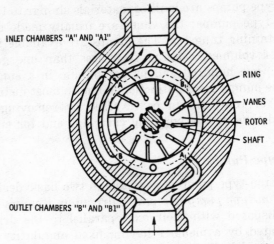

INLET CHAMBERS "A" AND "A1"

RING

VANES

ROTOR

SHAFT

OUTLET CHAMBERS "B" AND "B1"

Courtesy Vickers Incorporated

Fig. 6-6. The internal parts of a rotary vane-type pump.

loading (Fig. 6-6). This type of pump, like the gear-type pump, lends itself well to compound element combinations.

By carrying the single cam ring on thrust blocks that operate on bearings to permit movement either toward the center point or away from the center point under pressure, the pump can become a variable-displacement unit. Moving the cam ring to a concentric position produces no vane movement within the slots, thereby resulting in zero volume output. Moving the cam ring toward a more eccentric position causes in-and-out movement of the vanes and produces a volumetric-displacement in proportion to the amount of vane travel.

This variable-displacement feature is made functional in several ways. The most common methods are manual, mechanical, or pressure compensation. The pressure-compensated version utilizes a small spring at the bottom of the cam ring to force the ring toward neutral. Opposing this small spring, a much heavier spring acts against a differential piston. As pressure in the discharge port is applied to the differential piston, the pump cam ring moves toward neutral as the fluid force approaches the preset spring value. There is usually a limiting feature that permits adjustment to just short of complete neutral, to assure continuous lubrication of all internal wear surfaces and to deliver enough fluid to maintain the setting.

Vane-type pumps are built of materials similar to those used for gear-type pumps; the vanes are usually made of a steel alloy containing tungsten. The pumps are available in a wide variety of volumes, ranging from less than one gallon per minute to one hundred gallons per minute in a single rotor. Vane-type pumps are unidirectional, but, in most instances, the direction of rotation can be reversed by removing the end cover and turning the pumping cartridge end for end.

Piston-Type Pumps

The piston-type pump is available in two basic designs. The *axial piston-type pump* is a power-driven unit having multiple pistons disposed with their axes parallel to the drive shaft and actuated by a member having fixed angularity to these axes. The *radial piston-type pump* is a power-driven unit with a controlled volumetric output having multiple pistons disposed radially, actuated by a member having a fixed eccentricity.

These pumps are precision pieces of machinery and some of them are capable of producing pressures as high as 10,000 *psi*. The stroking of the pistons is accomplished by a variety of designs, the three major designs being the "swash-plate" or "angle-block," the "wobble-plate" (Fig. 6-7), and the "Thoma design."

Variable-displacement in the axial piston pump is accomplished by changing the angle of attack of the stroking member. A variety of controls can be utilized. Some of the more popular controls are: handwheel (Fig. 6-8), pressure-compensator, stem, servo, cylinder, and electric motor.

The radial piston pump accomplishes variable-displacement by moving the actuating member either toward or away from a concentric position similar to the method employed with the vane type of pumps.

The *hand-operated plunger-type pump* is a manually-operated piston-type unit, usually a single-piston pump, but it is sometimes either a double-piston or a double-acting single-piston pump. This type of pump is capable of rather high pressures, but of comparatively low volumes. The pressure and volume usually vary in inverse proportion to each other, and they are determined by the lever ratio as well as by the bore and stroke of the piston. This type of unit is most popular for non-

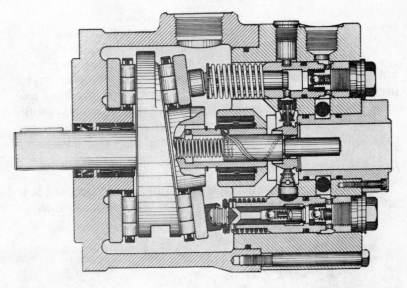

Fig. 6-7. Cutaway diagram of a variable-displacement piston-type pump of the "wobble-plate" design.

automated applications in which low cost and extreme portability are desirable.

The *duplex or triplex piston-type pump* is a combination of either two or three parallel pistons adapted to a power drive. This type of pump is comparatively expensive, but it is highly desirable for production of unusually high pressures; some pumps are rated as high as 60,000 *psi* (Fig. 6-9).

Piston-type pumps are among the most expensive pumps available, but their higher efficiency and higher pressure capa-

Courtesy Dynex, Inc.

Fig. 6-8. A handwheel is used to accomplish variable displacement in this axial piston pump.

bilities are desirable for variable-speed transmissions, many press applications, and the more sophisticated machine tool applications. Since their use demands extreme care and cleanliness and finer filtration equipment, their superior performance capabilities can make the higher cost and care worthwhile.

Diaphragm-Type Pump

The diaphragm-type pump is also simple in design, and it is intended for low-volume, low-pressure applications, such as

Fig. 6-9. Piston-type pump combining parallel pistons to produce unusually high pressures (as high as 60,000 psi).

Courtesy Kobe, Inc.

80

those required for fuel pumps. One variation of this type of pump, however, is the air-operated diaphragm (or in some instances, the air-operated piston) which is used to intensify an already confined fluid. This latter type of unit is sometimes referred to as an "intensifier" or "booster," and it is capable of boosting fluid pressures to extremely high values, based on the ratio of air displacement to fluid displacement per cycle.

Other, less conventional, pump designs are available, such as the *lobe-type pump* (De Laval) and the *screw-type pump* (Moyno), both of which produce a smooth, quiet flow. The characteristics of these pumps and other unusual pump designs can be studied by referring to the literature of the manufacturers of these specialty pumps.

AIR COMPRESSORS

The air compressor in the pneumatic system is comparable to the pump in the hydraulic system. The mechanical details of the two are similar—the latter pumping a *noncompressible fluid* to a captive system, and the air compressor pumping a *compressible gas* to a captive system. This difference is responsible for the notable differences between the two units. The compressing of air into a smaller volume gives rise to some problems that do not exist in the pressurizing of a fluid.

In handling these problems, design variations and modifications are found in air compressors that are not present in fluid pumps. For example, lubrication of a hydraulic pump is accomplished almost entirely by the fluid being pumped, but special provision for lubrication must be made for the air compressor. The heat of compression must be removed from the pumping element by means of cooling fins or water jackets. On being compressed, the air must, in most instances, be stored in a suitable pressure vessel; whereas a hydraulic fluid is usually pressurized at a rate that nearly approximates the demand. Atmospheric conditions, such as temperature, humidity, and foreign matter, affect the operation of air systems more than they affect the operation of hydraulic systems. Many different design approaches to the problems that arise in the mechanics of compressing gases can be found. A cursory look at some of the various compressor designs points toward a better understanding of compressor operation, of the problems, and of how they are dealt with in the different designs that are used in pneumatic systems.

All air compressors are either single-stage or multiple-stage machines. The *single-stage air compressor* raises the pressure of the gas from atmospheric pressure to the final pressure by means of a single compression stroke. The single-stage air compressor may be either a single-piston or a multiple-piston design. The *multiple-stage air compressor* raises the pressure of the gas from atmospheric pressure to an intermediate-pressure value by means of the first-stage piston, delivering the partially compressed gas to a second (smaller) piston which increases the pressure to a still higher value and delivers the gas either to the air receiver or to the additional stages. Working pressures above 100 to 125 *psi* are impractical, in most instances, with single-staging; therefore, multiple-staging is almost invariably used to obtain pressures above 125 *psi*.

Lubrication systems in air compressors resemble those employed in internal combustion engines. This means that the lubrication system is more complicated than for pumps in which lubrication is accomplished by the fluid that is being pumped.

The problem of disposing of the heat of compression presents another basis for classification—air-cooled and water-cooled units. Air-cooled units employ heat-radiating fins on the cylinder housing, the cylinder cover, and the discharge line. In the multiple-stage units, fins are also provided between stages, and this device is called an "intercooler." Water-cooled units utilize the same type of water jackets and radiator-type heat-exchanger systems that are found in the automobile.

In addition to the cooling provisions that are built into the compressor unit, it is usually advisable to pass the compressed gas through an additional water-cooled unit after it leaves the compressor. This unit is called an "aftercooler," and is described in a later chapter.

In general, air compressors may be classified as either low-speed machines or high-speed machines. The larger single-piston machine is a typical example of the low-speed air compressor. This type of unit operates at speeds in the 300 to 500 *rpm* range. This compressor is an "unbalanced" machine, and it should be mounted on and firmly bolted to a well-anchored concrete base of adequate mass to absorb the vibration and pulsation that is generated by the unit. The high-speed air compressor (multiple-piston) quite closely resembles the automotive engine, and it usually operates at speeds in the 900 to 1200 *rpm* range. The manufacturers of these high-speed units point out that these speeds are roughly equivalent to operating an automobile at an approximate road speed of 23 *mph*. The high-speed air compressors are of the "balanced" design, and they do not require extremely massive bases for mounting.

Air compressors are further classified as: piston-type (reciprocating); vane-type; lobe-type; rotary (centrifugal); or diaphragm-type machines. They may also be classified as either stationary or portable, with the portable type usually being driven by a gasoline or diesel engine.

Air compressors vary in size from ⅛-horsepower to 1000-horsepower machines, or even larger. Size, however, is usually stated in terms of cubic feet per minute, or *cfm*. This term indicates free-air, or noncompressed atmospheric volume. When making comparisons of different compressor ratings, the method by which each manufacturer arrives at his advertised rating should be noted. This rating may be determined by calculating the volumetric displacement of the compressing elements (labeled "*cfm* displacement"). Some compressor manufacturers, however, rate their machines on the volume of free air actually delivered by the machine, which is an actual performance rating. Although the latter method usually results in a lower rating than the displacement rating, it is normally considered to be a more true and more significant rating.

REVIEW QUESTIONS

1. List four main types of pumps.
2. What is the basic difference between the axial piston-type pump and the radial piston-type pump?
3. In what types of applications are rotary pumps commonly used?
4. List three types of air compressors.
5. What provisions are usually made for cooling in pneumatic systems?

7

Fluid
Lines
and
Fittings

The efficiency of a fluid power system is often limited by the lines (fluid carriers) which carry the fluid operating medium from one fluid power component to another. The purpose of these carriers is to provide leakproof passages at whatever operating pressure may be required in a system. A poorly planned system of fluid carriers for the system often results in component malfunctions due to: restrictions which create back pressure in the components; loss of speeds, which reduce efficiency; and broken carriers (especially in high-pressure systems), which create fire hazards and other problems. Selection of the proper carrier is as important as the proper selection of the fluid components.

Fluids may be directed through either lines or manifolds. Fluid lines or piping fall into three categories: (1) rigid; (2) semirigid, or tubing; and (3) flexible, or hose. In many instances, all three categories are employed in a single fluid system. The pressures involved and the fluid medium used determine, to a great extent, the type of carrier and the connectors and fittings.

RIGID PIPE

Steel pipe is the original type of carrier used in fluid power systems, and it is available in four different weights, as follows:

1. *Standard (STD), or Schedule 40.* This pipe (seamless) is designed for test pressure of 700 *psi* in the ⅛" size to 1100 *psi* in the 2" size.
2. *Extra strong (XS), or Schedule 80.* This weight of pipe is used in the medium pressure range of hydraulic systems. This pipe (seamless) is designed for test pressures of 850 *psi* for ⅛" size to 1600 *psi* in the 2" size (Grade B).
3. *Schedule 160.* This pipe is designed for test pressures up to 2500 *psi*.
4. *Double extra heavy (XXS).* This pipe is also used for test pressures up to 2500 *psi*, even though the wall thickness is somewhat heavier.

Sizes of pipe are listed by the nominal inside diameter (I.D.) which is actually a misnomer. The sizes are nearly equivalent to Schedule 40, but there is a difference. For example, the inside diameter of a ¼" Schedule 40 pipe is 0.364", and the I.D. of a ½" Schedule 40 pipe is 0.622".

As the schedule number of the pipe increases, the wall thickness also increases. This means that the inside diameter of the pipe for each nominal size is smaller, but the O.D. of the pipe for each nominal size remains constant (Table 7-1).

Some of the fittings that are used with steel pipe are tees, crosses, elbows, unions, street elbows, etc. Pipe fittings are listed in nominal pipe sizes.

Steel pipe is one of the least expensive of the fluid carriers for hydraulic fluid so far as the materials costs are concerned, but the installation costs often consume considerable man-hours in comparison to installation costs of some types of fluid carriers. Pipe is applicable to handling large fluid volumes and to running long lines of fluid carriers. Pipe is commonly used on suction lines to pumps and for short connections between two components. It is also useful on piping assemblies that are seldom disassembled. Pipe provides rigidity for holding various components in position, such as the valves that are designed for "in-line mounting" with no other method of support. Pipe

Table 7-1. Sizes of Steel Pipe

Nominal Pipe Size in.	Outside Diameter of Pipe in.	Schedule 40 (Standard)		Schedule 80 (Extra Heavy)		Schedule 160		Double Extra Heavy	
		Pipe ID-in.	Burst Press-psi	Pipe ID-in.	Burst Press-psi	Pipe ID-in.	Burst Press-psi	Pipe ID-in.	Burst Press-psi
⅛	0.405	—	—	—	—	—	—	—	—
¼	0.540	0.364	16,000	0.302	22,000	—	—	—	—
⅜	0.675	0.493	13,500	0.423	19,000	—	—	—	—
½	0.840	0.622	13,200	0.546	17,500	0.466	21,000	0.252	35,000
¾	1.050	0.824	11,000	0.742	15,000	0.614	21,000	0.434	30,000
1	1.315	1.049	10,000	0.957	13,600	0.815	19,000	0.599	27,000
1¼	1.660	1.380	8,400	1.278	11,500	1.160	15,000	0.896	23,000
1½	1.900	1.610	7,600	1.500	10,500	1.338	14,800	1.100	21,000
2	2.375	2.067	6,500	1.939	9,100	1.689	14,500	1.503	19,000
2½	2.875	2.469	7,000	2.323	9,600	2.125	13,000	1.771	18,000
3	3.500	3.068	6,100	2.900	8,500	2.624	12,500	—	—

should be cleaned thoroughly before it is installed in a fluid power system.

SEMIRIGID (TUBING)

Two types of steel tubing are utilized in hydraulic systems, as recommended by *JIC* hydraulic standards. These types of tubing are *seamless* and *electric-welded*. Tubing sizes are measured on the outside diameter (O.D.) of the tubing. Seamless steel tubing is manufactured from a highly ductile, dead-soft, annealed, low-carbon steel, with a chemical percentage of: carbon, 0.08-0.18; manganese, 0.30-0.60; phosphorous, 0.50 maximum; and sulfur, 0.55 maximum. The physical properties include: a tensile strength of 55,000 *psi*, maximum; Rockwell Hardness B65, maximum; and an elongation in 2 inches of 35 percent, minimum. In tubes with an O.D. of 3/8" and/or a wall thickness of 0.035, a minimum elongation of 30 percent is permitted. The diameter of the tubing shall not vary from that specified by more than the limits shown in Table 7-2.

Table 7-2. Specifications For Tubing Diameters

Nominal, O.D.	O.D. (Inches)	I.D. (Inches)
¼ to ½ in., incl.	±0.003	———
Above ½ to 1½ in., incl.	±0.005	±0.005
Above 1½ to 3½ in., incl.	±0.010	±0.010

The process used for making steel tubing is the cold drawing of pierced or hot-extruded billets. Table 7-3 shows the nominal sizes of seamless steel tubing that are readily available for hydraulic systems.

Electric-welded steel tubing is manufactured by shaping a cold-rolled strip of steel into a tube and then performing a welding and drawing operation. The chemical and physical properties of electric-welded steel tubing are similar to those of seamless steel tubing. In order to use steel tubing (or any other type of tubing) in a fluid power system, it is necessary to attach some type of fitting to each end of the tubing. Numerous methods are employed to accomplish this; but, in the final analysis, the fitting holds the tubing securely, providing a leak-proof assembly that can withstand the pressures for which it

Table 7-3. Steel Tubing Sizes and Safety Factors (SAE 1010)

Tube O.D.	Fitting Size	4/1 SAFETY FACTOR — Working Pressure in psi.				5/1 SAFETY FACTOR — Working Pressure in psi.		
		1000	2000	3000	5000	1000	2000	3000
⅛	2	.020	.020	.020	.025	.020	.020	.020
³⁄₁₆	3	.020	.020	.020	.035	.020	.020	.028
¼	4	.020	.020	.028	.049	.020	.022	.035
⁵⁄₁₆	5	.020	.025	.035	.056	.020	.028	.042
⅜	6	.020	.028	.042	.072	.020	.035	.049
½	8	.020	.042	.056	.095	.025	.049	.065
⅝	10	.025	.042	.072	.120	.032	.058	.083
¾	12	.028	.058	.083	.134	.035	.072	.109
⅞	14	.035	.072	.095	.165	.042	.083	.120
1	16	.042	.083	.109	.180	.049	.095	.134
1¼	20	.049	.095	.134	.238	.058	.120	.165
1½	24	.058	.120	.165	.284	.072	.134	.203
2	32	.072	.148	.220	.375	.095	.180	.259

Tube O.D.	Fitting Size	7.5/1 SAFETY FACTOR — Working Pressure in psi.				10/1 SAFETY FACTOR — Working Pressure in psi.		
		1000	2000	3000	5000	1000	2000	3000
⅛	2	.020	.020	.025	.042	.020	.025	.035
³⁄₁₆	3	.020	.025	.042	.065	.020	.035	.056
¼	4	.020	.035	.058	.095	.022	.049	.072
⁵⁄₁₆	5	.022	.042	.065	.109	.028	.056	.083
⅜	6	.025	.058	.083	.134	.035	.072	.109
½	8	.035	.072	.109	.220	.049	.095	.134
⅝	10	.042	.095	.134	.220	.058	.120	.180
¾	12	.058	.109	.148	.259	.072	.134	.203
⅞	14	.065	.120	.180	.320	.083	.165	.238
1	16	.072	.134	.203	.350	.095	.180	.259
1¼	20	.095	.180	.259	.450	.120	.238	.350
1½	24	.109	.203	.320	.500	.134	.284	.450
2	32	.134	.284	.400	—	.180	.375	—

was designed. In some instances, the fitting is welded to the tubing; in other applications (air systems), friction between the tubing and the fitting is sufficient to hold the pressure. An assembly in which a sleeve is brazed to the tubing, and the nut is then screwed onto the fitting, is shown in Fig. 7-1. A sleeve

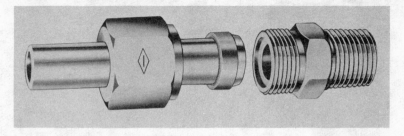

Fig. 7-1. An assembly in which a sleeve is brazed to the tubing and the nut is then screwed onto the fitting.

that digs into the tubing wall when the nut is tightened on the fitting is shown in Fig. 7-2. Some of the fittings that are most commonly used, such as tees, elbows, crosses, and straights are shown in Fig. 7-3.

Other types of tubing employed in fluid power systems are:

1. *Copper tubing.* This type of tubing is often found on air circuits which are not subject to *JIC* standards. Due to its

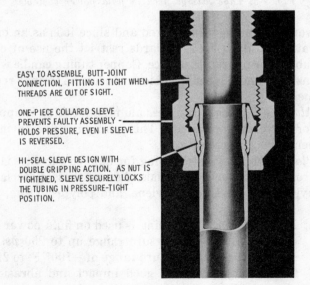

EASY TO ASSEMBLE, BUTT-JOINT CONNECTION. FITTING IS TIGHT WHEN THREADS ARE OUT OF SIGHT.

ONE-PIECE COLLARED SLEEVE PREVENTS FAULTY ASSEMBLY – HOLDS PRESSURE, EVEN IF SLEEVE IS REVERSED.

HI-SEAL SLEEVE DESIGN WITH DOUBLE GRIPPING ACTION. AS NUT IS TIGHTENED, SLEEVE SECURELY LOCKS THE TUBING IN PRESSURE-TIGHT POSITION.

Fig. 7-2. A fitting for high-pressure tubing in which the sleeve of the fitting grips the tubing.

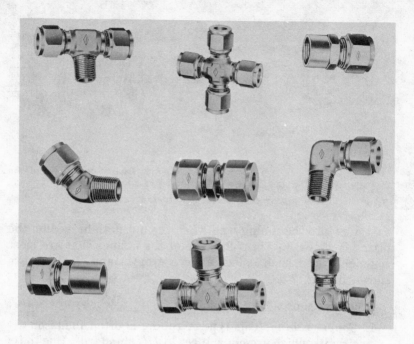

Fig. 7-3. Tube fittings used in fluid power systems.

work-hardening when flared and since it is as an oil-oxidation catalyst, *JIC* standards restrict the use of copper tubing for hydraulic service. Copper tubing can be worked easily in making bends, which reduces the fittings requirements.

2. *Aluminum tubing.* Seamless aluminum tubing is approved for low-pressure systems. This tubing has fine flaring and bending characteristics.

3. *Plastic tubing.* Plastic tubing for fluid power lines is made from several basic materials. Among these materials are nylon, polyvinyl, polyethylene, and polypropylene.

    a. *Nylon tubing.* This tubing is used on fluid power applications in the low-pressure range up to 250 *psi*. It is suitable for a temperature range of −100° F. to 225° F. This tubing possesses good impact and abrasion resistance; it can be stored without deteriorating or becoming brittle, and it is not affected by hydraulic fluids. One of the newer developments is the self-storing type of nylon tubing which looks like a coil spring, and is very popular for use on pneumatic tools.

b. *Polyvinyl chloride tubing.* For air lines with pressures up to 125 *psi*, this type of tubing may be used. Temperatures should not exceed 100° F. continuously. It may be used intermittently for temperatures up to 160° F.

c. *Polyethylene tubing.* This is an ideal tubing for pneumatic service, and it is also used for other fluids at low pressures. It possesses great dimensional stability and resists most chemicals and solvents. Polyethylene tubing is manufactured in several different colors, which lends it readily to color coding. Tubing sizes are usually available up to, and including, ½" O.D.

d. *Polypropylene tubing (Impolene TM).* This type of tubing is suitable for operating conditions with temperatures of −20° F. to +280° F., and it can be sterilized repeatedly with steam. It possesses surface hardness and elasticity that provide good abrasion resistance. It is usually available in sizes up to, and including, ½" O.D. and in natural or black colors.

FLEXIBLE PIPING (HOSE)

Hose is employed in a fluid power system in which the movement of one component of the system is related to another component. An example of this utilization is a pivot-mounted cylinder that moves through an arc while the valve to which the cylinder is connected with fluid lines remains in a stationary position. Hose may be used in either a pneumatic system or a hydraulic system.

Many different types of hose are used in fluid power systems, and nearly all of these types of hose have three things in common. They are:

1. *A tube or inner liner which resists penetration by the fluid being used.* This tube should be smooth to reduce friction. Some of the materials used for the tube are neoprene, Buna N, synthetic rubber, etc.

2. *A reinforcement which may be in the form of rayon braid, fabric braid, wire braid, or spiral-wound wire.* The

strength of the hose is determined by the number of thicknesses and type of reinforcement. If more than one thickness of reinforcement is used, a synthetic type of separator is utilized. A three-wire braid type of hose is made of three layers of wire braid.

3. *An outer cover to protect the inner portion of the hose and to enable the hose to resist heat, weather, abrasion, etc.* This cover can be made of synthetic rubber, neoprene, woven metal, or fabric.

Courtesy Imperial Eastman Corporation

Fig. 7-4. Section of hose assembly showing the layers of material, including the inner liner, reinforcement, and outer cover.

The nominal size of hose is specified by inside diameter (I.D.), such as $\frac{3}{16}''$, $\frac{1}{4}''$, $\frac{3}{8}''$, $\frac{1}{2}''$, etc. The outside diameter of hose depends on the number of layers of wire braid, etc. Fluid power applications may require hose with working pressure ratings ranging from approximately 300 *psi* to 12,000 *psi*. Specifications for a typical two-wire braid hose can be found in Table 7-4. The hose and the couplings that are attached at each end of the hose make up the hose assembly for fluid power applications. Several methods are used to attach these couplings to the hose. Some of these are:

1. *Pressed on* by a mechanical crimping action. Production machines can be used to make large quantities of the assemblies.

2. *Screwed on* by removing the outer cover of the hose for a required distance that is marked on the shell of the fitting; the shell is then threaded onto the braid, and the male body can be screwed into the hose and shell assembly. In some types of couplings, it is unnecessary to remove the outer cover. Screwed on couplings can be disassembled and used again.

Table 7-4. Specifications For a Typical Two-Wire Braid Hose

SIZE		PRESSURE		BEND RADIUS
Hose I.D. In.	Hose O.D. In.	Recommended Maximum Working Pressure psi	Minimum Burst Pressure psi	Minimum Bending Radius In.
3/16	5/8	5,000	20,000	4
1/4	11/16	5,000	20,000	4
5/16	3/4	4,250	17,000	5
3/8	27/32	4,000	16,000	5
1/2	31/32	3,500	14,000	7
5/8	1 3/32	2,750	11,000	8
3/4	1 1/4	2,250	9,000	9 1/2
7/8	1 3/8	2,000	8,000	11
1	1 9/16	2,000	8,000	12
1 1/4	2	1,625	6,500	16 1/2
1 1/2	2 1/4	1,250	5,000	20
2	2 3/4	1,125	4,500	25

3. *Clamped* on by screwing the hose onto the coupling stem until it bottoms against the collar on the stem; then the hose clamp is attached with bolts. Some couplings require two bolts, and others require four bolts for tightening the clamp onto the hose.

4. *Pushed on* by merely pushing the hose onto the coupling. This type of coupling is used in low-pressure applications up to 250 *psi.* No tools, except a knife to cut the hose to length, are needed to make this type of assembly. This type of coupling is reusable.

Various types of ends that are used on hose couplings are shown in Fig. 7-5. This permits the user a wide choice for his application.

Hose assemblies are measured with respect to their overall length from the extreme end of one coupling to the extreme end of the other coupling (Fig. 7-6). In applications using elbow couplings, the length is measured from the centerline of the sealing surface of the elbow end to the centerline of the coupling on the opposite end.

The length of a hose assembly that is to be looped can be determined from Fig. 7-7. Also, the proper diameter of hose to assure proper performance of hose for hydraulic service can be determined in Fig. 7-8.

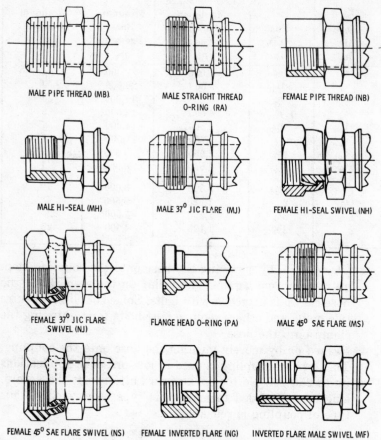

MALE PIPE THREAD (MB)

MALE STRAIGHT THREAD O-RING (RA)

FEMALE PIPE THREAD (NB)

MALE HI-SEAL (MH)

MALE 37° JIC FLARE (MJ)

FEMALE HI-SEAL SWIVEL (NH)

FEMALE 37° JIC FLARE SWIVEL (NJ)

FLANGE HEAD O-RING (PA)

MALE 45° SAE FLARE (MS)

FEMALE 45° SAE FLARE SWIVEL (NS)

FEMALE INVERTED FLARE (NG)

INVERTED FLARE MALE SWIVEL (MF)

Courtesy Imperial Eastman Corporation

Fig. 7-5. Common types of ends used on hose couplings.

In applications in which it is desirable to disconnect one end of a hose assembly repeatedly, quick-disconnect couplings are recommended. These couplings not only save considerable time in making or breaking the connection, but a properly chosen coupling provides positive shut-off, so that the fluid is not lost. A quick-disconnect coupling with double shut-off is shown in

Fig. 7-9; when the coupling is disconnected, the valved nipple and the valved coupler prevent the escape of fluid. Quick-disconnect couplings are also furnished in various other combinations, such as a single shut-off coupling with a plain nipple and a valved coupler and a no-shut-off coupler with a plain nipple and a plain coupler. Quick-disconnect couplings are available in a wide range of sizes from ¼″ to 4″ pipe size. Larger sizes are

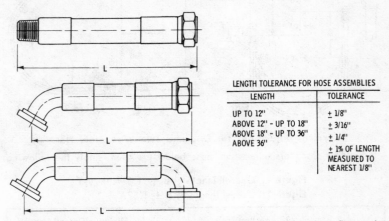

LENGTH TOLERANCE FOR HOSE ASSEMBLIES

LENGTH	TOLERANCE
UP TO 12″	± 1/8″
ABOVE 12″ - UP TO 18″	± 3/16″
ABOVE 18″ - UP TO 36″	± 1/4″
ABOVE 36″	± 1% OF LENGTH MEASURED TO NEAREST 1/8″

Fig. 7-6. Method of measuring the length of a hose assembly.

usually available as "specials." Various metals, such as brass, aluminum, stainless steel, and alloy steel are used. Seals in these couplings depend on the type of service involved. The fitting connections on the ends of the couplings are available in several forms, such as: Female (NPT), Male (NPT), Hose Shank, Female (SAE), Male Flare, Bulkhead, etc.

MANIFOLDS

Manifolds are designed to eliminate piping, to reduce joints which are often a source of leakage, to conserve space, and to help streamline modern-day equipment. Manifolds are usually one of the following types: (1) sandwich; (2) cast; (3) drilled; and (4) fabricated-tube. The "sandwich" type of manifold is made of flat plates in which the center plate or plates are machined for the passages, and the porting is drilled in the outer plates. The passages are then bonded together to make a leakproof assembly. The cast type of manifold is designed with cast passages and drilled porting. The casting may be steel, iron, bronze, or aluminum, depending on the fluid medium to be used. In the drilled type of manifold, all of the porting and

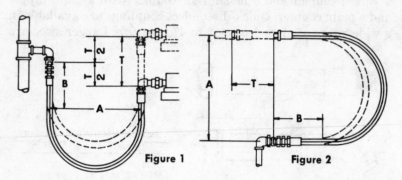

Figure 1 Figure 2

Typical Dimensions for One-and Two-Wire Braid Hose

If bending diameters other than those below are used, apply the following formulas:

Figure 1: Overall length = B + 1.57A + ½T
Figure 2: Overal length = B + 1.57A ± T

I.D. of Hose	"B" Constant for Straight Portion Including Coupling	Min. "A"	Minimum Overall Length	
			Fig. 1	Fig. 2
³⁄₁₆"	10"	8"	23" + ½T	23" + T
¼"	10"	8"	23" + ½T	23" + T
⅜"	10"	10"	26" + ½T	26" + T
½"	12"	14"	34" + ½T	34" + T
¾"	14"	19"	44" + ½T	44" + T
1"	16"	22"	51" + ½T	51" + T
1¼"	18"	32"	68" + ½T	68" + T
1½"	20"	44"	87" + ½T	87" + T
2"	20"	48"	95" + ½T	95" + T

Courtesy Imperial Eastman Corporation

Fig. 7-7. Typical dimensions for one-wire and two-wire braid hose in determining length.

passages are drilled in a block of metal. The fabricated-tube type of manifold is made of tubing to which the various sections have been welded. This makes an assembly which may contain welded flange connections, valve subplates, male or female pipe connectors, etc. These assemblies are usually produced in large quantities for use on the hydraulic systems of

Chart for Ratio Determination of Correct Hose Size to Assure Proper Hose Performance

Example: At 10 gallons per minute, determine size of hose assembly within recommended velocity range.

Solution: Lay straightedge at 10 gallons per minute on the left-hand column and at 10 feet per second (center of recommended velocity range) on the right-hand column. The hose size in the center column nearest the straightedge is the correct size. In this example, ¾" is the correct hose size.

For suction lines, use the recommended velocity for intake lines, following the same procedure.

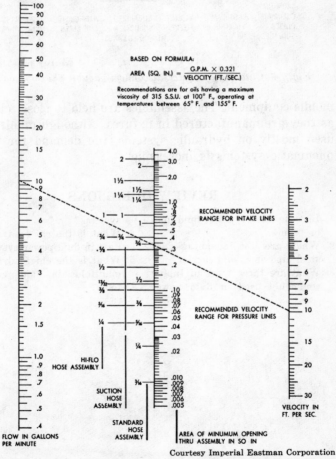

BASED ON FORMULA:

$$\text{AREA (SQ. IN.)} = \frac{\text{G.P.M.} \times 0.321}{\text{VELOCITY (FT./SEC.)}}$$

Recommendations are for oils having a maximum viscosity of 315 S.S.U. at 100° F., operating at temperatures between 65° F. and 155° F.

Fig. 7-8. Method of determining the correct size of hose.

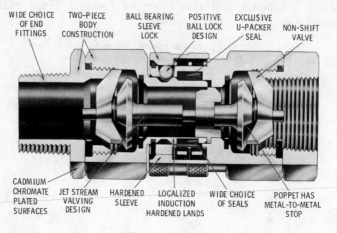

WIDE CHOICE OF END FITTINGS   TWO-PIECE BODY CONSTRUCTION   BALL BEARING SLEEVE LOCK   POSITIVE BALL LOCK DESIGN   EXCLUSIVE U-PACKER SEAL   NON-SHIFT VALVE

CADMIUM CHROMATE PLATED SURFACES   JET STREAM VALVING DESIGN   HARDENED SLEEVE   LOCALIZED INDUCTION HARDENED LANDS   WIDE CHOICE OF SEALS   POPPET HAS METAL-TO-METAL STOP

Courtesy Snap-Tite, Inc.

Fig. 7-9. Cutaway of "quick-disconnect" double shut-off coupling.

mobile equipment. The assemblies are held to close tolerances, as they are manufactured in fixtures. Although manifolds are used mostly on hydraulic systems, the demand for them in pneumatic systems is increasing.

REVIEW QUESTIONS

1. List the three types of fluid lines or piping.
2. What are the advantages of steel pipe as a fluid carrier?
3. What are three types of tubing commonly used in fluid power systems?
4. What is the chief advantage of hose in fluid power systems?
5. What is the chief advantage of manifolds in fluid power systems?

8

Filters, Lubricators, and Dryers

To obtain maximum efficiency from a fluid power system, the medium used in that system must be properly conditioned at all times. Various devices are utilized for this purpose. Some of them are discussed in this chapter.

If compressed air is to be used as the medium, provisions must be made for proper installation of the piping, and the proper type of filters and lubricators must be employed. The pneumatic systems must be installed properly to provide greater efficiency (Fig. 8-1).

FILTERS

Various types of filters are used in a pneumatic system. Some types of filters are merely strainers which remove only the large "chunks" of scale and other impurities that collect in the air lines. Other types of filters remove particles as small as five microns, and even smaller. A micron is a unit equal in length to one-millionth of a meter, or 0.000039 inch.

Various filtering methods are used to separate impurities, as well as water, from the compressed air in the filter. Among

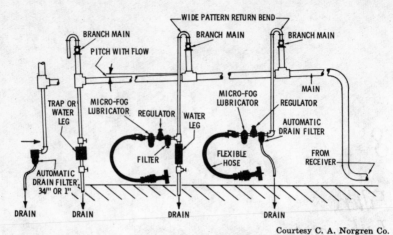

Fig. 8-1. Air lines should be installed properly for greater efficiency.

these methods are mechanical, filtration, and a combination of the two methods. Filters should remove as much of the impurities as possible, with the least amount of pressure drop. A mechanical-type filter in which the compressed air causes

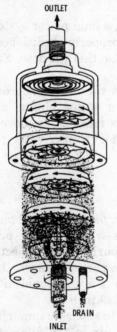

Fig. 8-2. A mechanical-type filter.

100

four rotors to rotate at high speed is shown in Fig. 8-2. The action of the rotors is similar to that of a centrifuge in a cream separator. The impurities, which are considerably heavier than the compressed air, are directed against the outer walls of the filter housing by centrifugal force. Then they drop to the bottom of the filter housing and into a trap. Two of the rotors

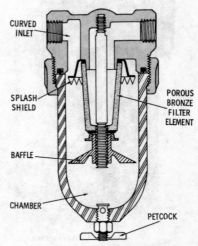

CURVED INLET

SPLASH SHIELD

POROUS BRONZE FILTER ELEMENT

BAFFLE

CHAMBER

PETCOCK

Fig. 8-3. Section of filter with a porous metal element.

revolve in one direction and the other two rotors revolve in the opposite direction. The sudden reversal of the air stream provides a cleaning action for removing the impurities, and clean filtered air leaves the filter through the outlet port.

Filter elements are made from a number of different materials, such as porous materials, fine-mesh screen, phenolic-impregnated cellulose, felt, stone, etc. A filter element made from a porous material is shown in Fig. 8-3. In this type of filter, the heavy impurities are expelled by the action of centrifugal force, are collected on the sides of the bowl, and then move downward to the petcock where they can be drained off. The dry air then advances through the porous bronze filter element where the fine particles are removed. This type of porous filter element removes particles as small as 40 microns in normal size. However, porous elements are available that can provide even finer filtration, but the pressure drop through the element must be considered.

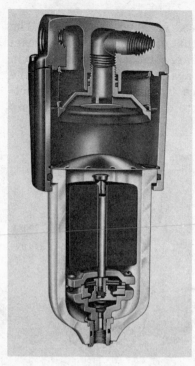

Fig. 8-4. Cutaway view showing a filter element that is made of a fine-mesh screen.

Courtesy C. A. Norgren Co.

A filter element made of fine-mesh screen is shown in Fig. 8-4. This element is designed for 75-micron removal and is constructed of Monel wire. The filter is equipped with an automatic drain feature which makes it desirable for use in locations which are inaccessible and may be overlooked easily. The automatic-drain feature also aids in reducing the service requirements of a maintenance man.

A filter element constructed of a cellulose material which is impregnated with a plastic material is illustrated in Fig. 8-5. This material is made in the form of a ribbon and is edge-wound on a mandrel to produce a cylindrical element. The action of the compressed air passing through the element is known as "edge filtration." The air passes from outside the element to the inside, and the element can be "back-washed" when it becomes dirty.

Bowl-type filters may be equipped with either plastic or metal bowls. Bowl guards are also available for filters with plastic bowls. The guards are made of metal with perforations

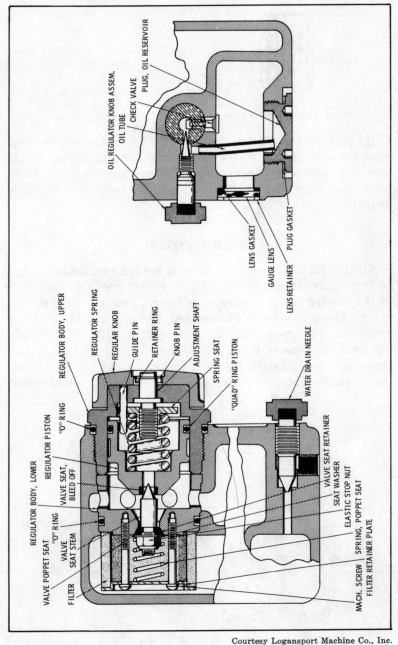

OIL REGULATOR KNOB ASSEM.
OIL TUBE
CHECK VALVE
PLUG, OIL RESERVOIR

LENS GASKET
GAUGE LENS
LENS RETAINER
PLUG GASKET

REGULATOR SPRING
REGULATOR BODY, UPPER
REGULAR KNOB
GUIDE PIN
RETAINER RING
KNOB PIN
ADJUSTMENT SHAFT
SPRING SEAT
"QUAD" RING PISTON

"O" RING

WATER DRAIN NEEDLE

REGULATOR BODY, LOWER
REGULATOR PISTON
VALVE SEAT, BLEED OFF

VALVE SEAT RETAINER
SEAT WASHER
ELASTIC STOP NUT

"O" RING
VALVE POPPET SEAT
VALVE SEAT STEM
FILTER

MACH. SCREW   SPRING, POPPET SEAT
SEAT
FILTER RETAINER PLATE

Courtesy Logansport Machine Co., Inc.

Fig. 8-5. A filter with a phenolic-impregnated cellulose element.

(Fig. 8-6), so that the contents in the bowls are visible. The most popular sizes of filters range up to, and including, ¾-in. pipe size. However, larger sizes of filters are available. Most bowl-type filters are available with some type of automatic-drain.

LUBRICATORS

Air line lubricators should provide enough lubrication to aid in keeping corrosion at a minimum and to provide protection to the moving parts of valves, cylinders, and motors; yet, the system should not be overlubricated, because the action of the components becomes sluggish. A number of different methods are used to disperse the lubricant into the air lines. Some of these are: fog, mist, drop, wick, or siphon. An air line lubricator that produces an oil fog is shown in Fig. 8-7. Compressed

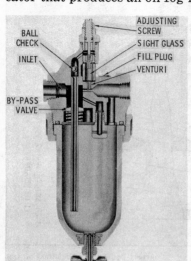

Fig. 8-7. Air line lubricator that produces an oil fog.

air enters the lubricator and is channeled in one or two directions, depending on the rate of flow. At a low rate of flow, all of the compressed air passes through a high-velocity venturi section where it is mixed with metered oil droplets to produce a fine atomized oil mist that is directed out of the lubricator to the downstream equipment. When higher rates of compressed air are required, the excess air opens a patented spring-loaded by-pass valve and compressed air flows around the restricted venturi section; it then blends with the venturi-produced oil-laden air. The oil-laden compressed air then leaves the lubricator and moves downstream to lubricate the components of the system. The adjusting screw at the top of the lubricator meters the amount of oil that passes into the sight glass section. The ball check prevents the oil from returning to the reservoir when oil flow is stopped.

A lubricator that produces an oil mist is diagrammed in Fig. 8-8. Particles of oil that are 2 microns in size, and smaller, enter into the air line. The larger particles of oil return to the oil

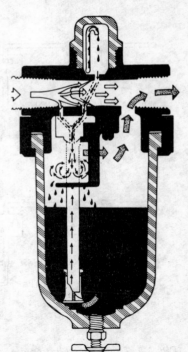

Fig. 8-8. Air line lubricator that produces an oil mist.

reservoir (bowl) and are reused. Approximately one drop of oil in each twenty drops actually enters the air to produce lubricated air. The remaining drops of oil are returned to the reservoir and reused.

Lubricators should be placed as near the components which are to be lubricated as possible. In short-stroke cylinders, injection-type lubricators are often utilized. Typical installation diagrams in which injection-type lubricators are used are shown in Fig. 8-9.

Lubricators are made with either plastic or metal bowls which are similar to those employed on filters. Bowl guards are also available. Some lubricators are manufactured with devices that make it unnecessary to shut off the air pressure when filling them with oil.

Air line lubricators are available in pipe sizes that range to 2 inches; however, the most common sizes are ¼", ⅜", ½", and ¾" pipe sizes. Lubricators should always be mounted in the vertical position. Various types of oil can be used in the

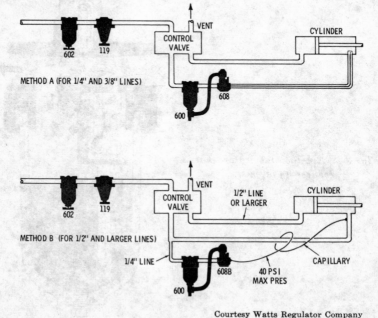

Courtesy Watts Regulator Company

Fig. 8-9. Typical installation diagrams in which injection-type lubricators are used.

lubricators; however, the manufacturer of the lubricator should be contacted for his recommendations.

AIR DRYERS

Some industries are required to use dry air in their operations. Among these industries are: food processing, packaging, textile, paint, petroleum, etc. Various types of drying equipment are employed. Although the air filters do a good job in

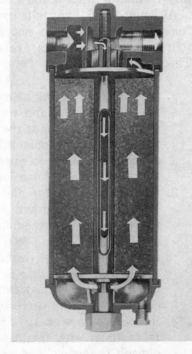

Fig. 8-10. Cutaway view of a compact manual-type dryer in which a dessicant is used.

removing moisture, further moisture removal is needed in many plants. Air dryers are employed to provide for additional moisture removal. A compact manual-type dryer in which a desiccant is used is shown in Fig. 8-10. The damp air enters the unit and passes down the center tube into the bottom chamber where the droplets separate out. The relatively clean air moves upward through a fine-mesh screen that keeps out dirt, and

107

then it flows into the full bed of desiccant where the dew point of the air is lowered. Then the air flows to the outlet and into the system. Other types of dryers that are available are the self-regenerating heatless dryers, the power-type dryers, etc.

HYDRAULIC FILTERS

Hydraulic filters are needed to aid in eliminating many of the potential causes of hydraulic system failures. Proper filters and proper filter maintenance are important in obtaining satisfactory results in a hydraulic system.

Although most hydraulic systems are considered to be the "closed" type, they are not free from contaminants. Four sources of contaminants are common in hydraulic systems. These are:

1. *Wear.* As the sliding members of components move, small particles of metal and seals enter the fluid. A typical example of this action is the movement of a cast-iron piston within a steel cylinder tube. Wear begins as soon as the cylinder is placed in operation, although it may not be visible to the eye for a long period of time.

2. *Formation of sludge and acids due to fluid breakdown.* When extreme heat and pressure are encountered, chemical reaction within the fluid causes sludge and acids which are harmful to the precision parts of the components to form. For example, resinous coatings may cause a valve spool to "freeze" within the valve body by forming on moving parts; or small orifices may become clogged. Acids cause pitting and corrosive conditions.

3. *Built-in contaminants in the manufacture of components.* In castings with intricate cored passages, core sand is difficult to remove, and small quantities of sand can enter the system as the fluid flows through the cored passages under high pressure. Lint and small metal chips are also encountered.

4. *Contaminants from outside the system.* Lint may enter the system if the filler cap on the oil reservoir is not replaced. Dirt that clings to the piston rod of a cylinder or to the stem of a valve may enter the system. Water or coolant may enter a system.

Factors that should be considered in selecting a hydraulic filter are: flow rate, pressure drop, degree of filtration, capacity, ease of servicing, compatibility with the fluid in the system, and pressure to which the filter is subjected. The filter in a hydraulic system can be located in a number of places. Some of these locations are:

Fig. 8-11. A sump-type filter equipped with magnetic rods for collecting minute particles of steel and iron.

Courtesy Marvel Engineering Company

1. *In the sump or oil reservoir.* This is a sump-type filter (Fig. 8-11). The filter should have a capacity twice that of the hydraulic pump in order to keep pressure drop at a minimum and to eliminate the possibility of cavitation in the pump.
2. *In the discharge line from the relief valve.* Since, in most systems, a considerable quantity of fluid passes through the discharge of the relief valve, a low-pressure filter with fine filtration is recommended. The filter should be equipped with a low-pressure by-pass valve to avoid filter or system failure. The capacity of the filter should be large enough to handle the full flow of the pump without imposing a back-pressure on the relief valve. Back-pressure on the exhaust of the relief valve can cause malfunctions within the system.
3. *In the by-pass line from the pump.* In by-pass line filtration, a small percentage (approximately 10 percent) of the flow from the pump passes through the by-pass filter, and returns to the reservoir as clean oil. A pressure-com-

pensated flow control should be installed between the pump and the filter to maintain constant flow at minimum pressure through the filter. An internal by-pass valve in the filter is recommended to avoid filter failure if the filter becomes clogged completely.

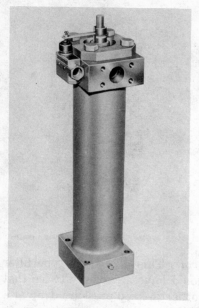

Fig. 8-12. A high-pressure filter equipped with a warning switch that provides a signal when the filter requires cleaning.

4. *In the pressure line between the pump and the directional control valve.* To protect the components of the system that are located beyond the pump, a high-pressure filter which can handle full pump pressure and flow is often employed. Although 25-micron filtration is an often-used standard in industry, a 5-micron, or less, filter is sometimes desirable if close-fitting parts are to be protected. The flow capacity through the filter should be as high as possible (four to five times pump capacity). A built-in by-pass relief valve should be incorporated within the filter, because the filter may become overloaded with contaminants. A high-pressure filter equipped with a warning switch that provides a signal when the filter requires cleaning is shown in Fig. 8-12.

5. *In the intake line between the sump and the pump.* The intake line filter is similar to the sump-type filter, except that it is encased and is mounted outside the reservoir. A 100-mesh filter is commonly used for hydraulic oils, and a 60-mesh filter is usually specified for aqueous-base fluids. The filter elements can be replaced without disturbing the piping (Fig. 8-13).

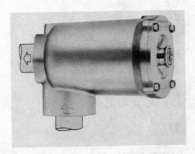

Fig. 8-13. Intake line filter placed between the sump and the pump.

Courtesy Marvel Engineering Company

6. *In the exhaust line between the four-way directional control valve and the reservoir.* The exhaust line filter is helpful when the bulk of the fluid is returned to the reservoir through the four-way directional control valve. However, if most of the fluid is returned through the relief valve or by-pass valve, this type of filter is of little value. When the return-line filter is used, it should have more capacity than the maximum flow of the return line, to reduce back-pressure to a minimum on the exhaust of the control valve. Sudden surges and shock can have a detrimental effect on the element in this type of filter.

REVIEW QUESTIONS

1. What is the purpose of a filter in a pneumatic system?
2. What types of filter elements are commonly used in filters in pneumatic systems?
3. Why is a lubricator necessary in compressed air systems?
4. Why is an air dryer necessary in a pneumatic system?
5. What is the purpose of the filter in a hydraulic system?

9

Temperature
Problems
and
Control

Temperature is an extremely significant factor in many fluid power systems. In order to anticipate and to provide adequately for the temperature, it is necessary to understand: why temperature problems occur; where temperature problems are likely to occur; how temperature affects the performance of the components and systems; and what provisions can and should be made to control temperature.

TEMPERATURE RISE IN PNEUMATIC SYSTEMS

In a pneumatic system, a decided rise in temperature is experienced, because work is performed to compress the air. This temperature rise is a result of frictional heat and some transposition of electrical or combustion energy into heat within the air. The temperature rise, although it may vary from one compressor to another, is inevitable, and it is referred to as "heat of compression." Conversely, when pressure is suddenly dissipated—as in the exhausting of a valve, cylinder, or vessel —the air absorbs heat from the surrounding material or atmosphere. As a result of this phenomenon, it is not unusual to encounter exhaust ports or lines that are supercooled, even to the point of collecting frost on the surfaces.

The temperature of the air in a compressed air supply system is significant in its relation to and in its effect on the moisture content entrained within that air volume. The capacity of air to hold moisture in suspension varies in direct proportion to its temperature. As air cools, or is cooled, its lowered capacity to hold the entrained moisture in suspension results in condensation of that moisture. The condensate then becomes a deterrent to the proper operation of components; the accumulation of sludges in orifices and seal grooves and the deterioration of mating surfaces due to the corrosive effect of moisture on many metals are results of this type of condensate.

A pressure drop that is caused by a flow of air within the enclosed system creates a comparable temperature drop, resulting in condensation of entrained moisture. Thus it is advisable to cool the compressed air immediately on its delivery from the compressor. This permits planned removal of the resulting condensate at the air receiver before it can be carried into the operating components of the air system. The most practical and most widely accepted unit for accomplishing this type of pre-system cooling is the aftercooler.

An *aftercooler* is in reality a "heat exchanger," and water is used to absorb the heat that is radiated from the compressed air. The aftercooler is usually of tubular construction, and consists of a bundle of interconnected, thin-walled, small-diameter tubes contained within a tubular water jacket (Fig. 9-1). The heat within the compressed air passes through the thin-walled tubing, and is carried away by the water flowing through the jacket. For the most efficient cooling action, it is recommended that the water flow from the air-discharge end of the after-

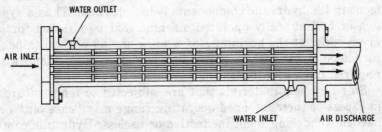

Fig. 9-1. Cutaway view of an aftercooler.

cooler toward the air-inlet end. Since an increase in air temperature parallels an increase in water temperature, this type of flow arrangement permits efficient cooling along the entire length of the unit.

This moisture-removal and air-cooling process provides an additional advantage in the form of safety. By controlling the temperature and by reducing the moisture content, the possibility of generating steam of explosive force is also removed.

TEMPERATURE RISE IN HYDRAULIC SYSTEMS

In a hydraulic system, the problem of heat is considerably different from that encountered in a pneumatic system. Heat not only causes hydraulic fluids to deteriorate but it also changes the characteristics of the fluid and the performance of the components within the system. Uncontrolled temperatures within a hydraulic system can either destroy or render ineffective many of the standard materials that are used in system components. Clearances of moving or mating parts made of dissimilar materials may be altered due to different coefficients of expansion. These changes may create excessive clearance flows or increased friction resistance, resulting in the creation of more heat.

One of the properties or characteristics of a hydraulic oil that helps to determine its performance within a hydraulic system is its viscosity, or resistance to flow. The viscosity of an oil changes as its temperature changes. The amount of change varies from one oil to another, and this amount of change per temperature variant is referred to as its "viscosity index." Since the inherent resistance to the flow of a fluid determines its rate of flow through a given orifice, any unwarranted temperature change can result in varying rates of movement in the hydraulic components being operated. Thus a system or hydraulically operated machine that is adjusted for a given speed at the beginning of a work day may alter its performance rate to such an extent that numerous adjustments are required during an operating period.

Standard seal materials that are subjected to temperatures in excess of their intended operating range may "cure out" or harden, rendering them ineffective or useless. Hydraulic components can be equipped with seals that are made from compounds that are capable of withstanding temperatures in excess of 500° F. These seals, however, are much more expensive than the standard seals, and they are only a partial answer to a problem that may be handled more easily by controlling the temperature of the fluid.

Most of the heat that is encountered in a hydraulic system originates at the pump unit. In the same manner that heat of compression is created in the air compressor, heat is also created or induced into the hydraulic fluid as a direct result of the work that is performed on the fluid in moving it and in pressurizing it. In the functioning of a hydraulic pump, extreme forces and much higher pressures are involved, with the result that higher frictional resistance is encountered within the working parts of the pump. Additional heat is added to the fluid at points in the system where additional frictional resistance is encountered. Liquids transfer heat at a slower rate than air, as indicated by the more moderate temperatures that prevail near geographical bodies of water. The tendency of the fluid to hold its heat results in a pyramiding of heat accumulation to the point where it becomes a problem within the hydraulic system.

The heat content of a hydraulic fluid is released to its surroundings at an accelerated rate on the release of fluid pressure. Thus heat concentrations can be found in the hydraulic system at places such as the relief valve or across any orifice in which there is a pressure differential. For this reason, additional heat concentrations occur at any spot in the system where a clearance flow or internal leakage occurs. Thus, a pump that loses its efficiency as a result of slippage or internal by-passing of the fluid on which it is performing work operates at progressively increasing temperatures, since additional wear of the pump parts contributes to an increasing slippage rate. This heat-generating condition tends to magnify itself as the elevated temperature reduces the viscosity of the fluid, permitting an even higher slippage rate.

It should be noted at this point that heat concentrations within a system should be looked for, since this is possible evidence of internal wear of the pump elements, control valves, and cylinder seals. Most hydraulic systems operate with greatest efficiency in a temperature range of 140° F. to 160°F. When the fluid temperature begins to exceed approximately 170° F., maintenance problems should be anticipated.

The most common remedy for excessive temperatures in a hydraulic system is the *heat exchanger*. The two main types of heat exchanger used in industry are the air-type which utilizes the "radiator" principle found in the automobile and the water-type which is similar in construction to the aftercooler described earlier. In systems where the oil temperature fluctuates widely due to intermittent usage of the system pressure, the addition of a temperature-controlled water valve at the water supply may help to maintain a more constant temperature level in the oil supply. This option can also appreciably reduce unnecessary water consumption.

Heat-exchanger units are more practical when they are installed in the line that returns the oil from the work components to the reservoir. Wherever possible, all returning oil, except for that returned in the drain lines, should be channeled through the heat-exchanger unit. Most heat-exchanger units are designed for the low pressures that are encountered in the return lines, but the high-pressure units are available at much greater cost. Occasionally, a condition may exist where it is imperative to install the cooling unit in the pressure line, but these conditions are rather uncommon.

Some work requirements lend themselves to other means of controlling, or at least reducing, the heat build-up within a hydraulic system. The variable-displacement pump is one practical approach to this problem. Since this type of pump reduces its volumetric pumping rate as the demand for fluid is satisfied in a system, less work is performed within the pump and thereby less heat is added to the system. In a molding press with a long curing cycle, for example, the variable-displacement pressure-compensated pump automatically adjusts itself to deliver only sufficient hydraulic fluid for maintaining the required pressure in the system.

A hydraulic application that encompasses a work cycle with built-in idle time suggests the use of a more simple method for reducing the work performed on the hydraulic fluid during the idle time. Two methods that are commonly used are:

1. A three-position operating valve with a spool configuration that permits the valve in centered position to by-pass the hydraulic fluid back to the hydraulic reservoir with only nominal pressurizing of the oil by the pump; if a

116

solenoid-operated, hydraulically piloted valve is used, adequate pressure must be provided for shifting the valve. This is usually accomplished by a 65-*psi* check valve in the tank line. Some of these valves are offered with this option built into the valve. Other valves do not have this feature, and they require this type of check valve to be installed in the tank line.

2. Another method of accomplishing unloading of the pump during idle time is the use of a pilot-operated relief valve that can be vented to the tank. The venting can be accomplished by either a manually operated or an electrically operated two-way valve. Piloting pressure can be provided by installing the back-pressure check valve in the tank line of the relief valve.

Either of the two foregoing methods appreciably reduces the amount of heat that is introduced into a hydraulic system, and either method reduces the amount of power consumed by the power source that drives the pump. In some systems it is wise to incorporate an unloading feature as well as the heat exchanger that was discussed previously.

Many hydraulic systems have been constructed only to discover, on being placed in operation, that they perform in the marginal area of the higher limits of temperature. These units soon progress to a condition of excessive temperatures caused by accelerated and premature deterioration of the components in the system.

The initial design of a hydraulic system offers many opportunities for gaining a few degrees in operating temperature, which may later prove to be extremely valuable in terms of more lengthy component life and more freedom from maintenance problems.

Heat is radiated or transferred from the hydraulic fluid in a system by means of all surfaces contacted by the fluid. The reservoir provides at least five surfaces whose total radiating area is determined by the size of the reservoir. The reservoir should be provided with risers or legs that provide 6 in. of minimum height above the floor. This permits proper air circulation across the bottom surface of the vessel, and eases the housekeeping efforts. It is strongly recommended that a reservoir should be adequate in size to contain a fluid volume of at least three times the *gpm* rating of the pump. Although increasing the size of the reservoir increases the surface area only arithmetically, the volume of fluid capacity increases geometrically. The fluid, however, thereby is permitted a longer rest period or idle time for the dissipation of heat through the walls of the reservoir. Therefore, advantage can be obtained by designing the reservoir oversized, when the question of its size is considered.

If occasional fluctuations in ambient temperatures are to be encountered, a rather simple, but inexpensive, device can be installed to gain several degrees of operating temperature by installing a hand-formed coil of tubing inside the reservoir, with the tube ends culminating through the reservoir wall in such a way that a flow of water can be passed through the tube when extra cooling is required. This device is not intended to substitute for a commercially designed and built heat exchanger, but it should be less expensive to provide if the heat problem is marginal.

Materials used in return or tank lines can also be responsible for a few marginal degrees of operating temperature. Since metal delivers a much greater heat-transfer rate than rubber, metal tubing or pipe should be used wherever possible. A further advantage can be gained by the use of "finned" tubing. This type of tubing can provide a much greater heat-transfer rate than common tubing or pipe.

A hydraulic power unit in the lower horsepower range may lend itself to the installation of a double-shaft motor to drive the pump. The extra shaft extension can then be used to attach a shrouded fan blade. A further refinement is to channel the return oil through a tubing coil placed directly in the path of the air current created thereby.

Whenever possible, the hydraulic unit should be placed in a location that permits free circulation of the cooling air across the entire system. A remote corner of the shop may be the ideal out-of-the-way spot, but practical experience strongly recommends that first consideration be given the cooling or heat dissipation factor.

None of the foregoing suggestions may appear to be important, but if every opportunity is utilized to eliminate the heat problem before it arises, greater success in the design and installation of hydraulic systems may be the result.

EFFECTS OF LOW AMBIENT TEMPERATURES

Unusually low ambient temperatures are also encountered occasionally with the use of a hydraulic system. In the same manner that an increase in oil operating temperature decreases the viscosity of the hydraulic fluid, a drastic increase in viscosity resulting from excessive cooling of the fluid can produce problems of equal magnitude. The extremely low temperatures that are encountered in some environments can produce viscosity changes that render hydraulic oils "nonpourable." This condition not only produces tremendous stresses within a hydraulic pump but it also creates overloads far in excess of design tolerances. In a unit driven by an electric motor, the starting torque of the electric motor may be exceeded. In gasoline engine or in diesel units, starting may be a problem.

When low ambient temperatures create problems, it may be necessary to install some means of heating the fluid to return its viscosity level to a workable value. The most common method of accomplishing this is to use an electric heating element of the submersible type that can be installed through the wall of the oil reservoir. This unit should be equipped with a thermostatic control, to eliminate the possibility of overheating. In remote installations where electric power is not available, a gas-operated unit or some other practical and available means is advisable.

REVIEW QUESTIONS

1. Why is temperature rise significant in a pneumatic system?
2. What is the purpose of the aftercooler in a pneumatic system?
3. What is the effect of temperature rise in a hydraulic system?
4. What is the effect of temperature rise on the viscosity of a hydraulic oil?
5. What is the effect of low ambient temperatures on a hydraulic system?

10

Hydraulics
or
Pneumatics

Whether to choose a hydraulic system or a pneumatic system for an application is often a difficult decision. Even the experts are not always absolutely certain in borderline decisions. Of course, in some applications it is obvious that a hydraulic system should be used, and in other instances it is obvious that a pneumatic system should be used. Some of the general rules, which are rather basic, that may be followed in choosing a fluid system are: (1) If a great amount of force is required, use hydraulics; (2) If high speeds and rapid response are desired, use pneumatics; and (3) If fine feeds are required and if force is not an important factor, use a combination of pneumatics and hydraulics. To be more explicit, if a press which must produce 600 tons of force is involved,then, under normal circumstances, hydraulics should be chosen for a number of reasons: (1) The cost of an air cylinder needed to produce a 600-ton force is prohibitive; (2) The cost of the volume of compressed air required to stroke a 600-ton press is extremely expensive; (3) The suitable materials needed to produce a cylinder of this size, as well as the equipment required to machine such a cylinder (especially if the press requires a long stroke), are not readily available; (4) Repair parts are extremely difficult to obtain; and (5) Control valves of sufficient capacity are of a special type and they are costly.

Air presses which produce a considerable amount of force are available, but they are usually designed with a linkage mechanism that produces a favorable lever advantage, such as a three-to-one advantage. This reduces the actual stroke of the press ram; but this condition is not objectionable in many applications, and this type of press still requires a considerable volume of compressed air (Fig. 10-1). These presses are often used for production assembly operations.

When high speeds are needed, a pneumatic system is usually preferable, although hydraulic systems are used on some types of high-cycling applications (often in excess of one hundred cycles per minute). Sometimes, when it is necessary to obtain several hundred cycles per minute with air directional control valves, the response time is very important. The response time of a directional control is the time interval between the initial input signal and full flow at a given pressure. The flow capacity and the shifting speed of the spool or flow director governs the response time. In a two-position direct-operated solenoid valve, the response time is measured from the moment the solenoid is energized until the spool reaches the position opposite that of the energized solenoid. Spools or flow directors that require only a short movement are helpful on high-cycling applications.

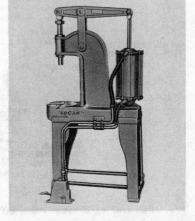

Fig. 10-1. An air-operated arbor press.

Courtesy Logansport Machine Co., Inc.

Compressed air is somewhat more difficult to control than hyraulic fluid, because it is "spongy" or compressible; it is often undesirable when it is used alone and fine feeds are required. When compressed air is used in conjunction with hydraulics, as shown in Fig. 10-2, highly accurate feeds can be obtained. These feeds may be as little as ⅛ in. per minute, which is considerably slower than can be normally maintained in an all-hydraulic system.

Cushioning of loads (when using compressed air) is sometimes difficult, especially if small-bore pneumatic cylinders are involved. For example, in 1″, 1½″, and sometimes in 2″ bore cylinders, sufficient air cannot be trapped to provide an effective cushion. Even the cushions that are longer than the standard-length cushions (usually ⅝″ to 1″ long) cannot do the job. If longer cushions are employed, "bounce" may create a problem, due to the air that is suddenly trapped within the cylinder.

Hydraulic cylinders with cushions, even in the smaller cylinder bores, can be used to produce a suitable deceleration pattern. If loads are being moved at high speeds on a freely moving slide or carriage, it may be necessary to use either longer cushions or deceleration valves to control the load properly and provide a smooth stop. An example of this type of application is the transfer of a large tray of television tubes from station X to station Y. Smooth acceleration and deceleration rates are

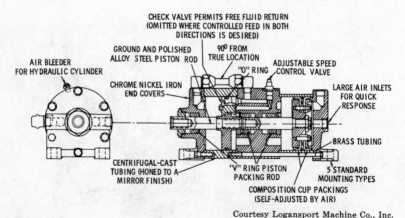

CHECK VALVE PERMITS FREE FLUID RETURN
(OMITTED WHERE CONTROLLED FEED IN BOTH
DIRECTIONS IS DESIRED)

GROUND AND POLISHED   90° FROM
ALLOY STEEL PISTON ROD   TRUE LOCATION

AIR BLEEDER   "O" RING   ADJUSTABLE SPEED
FOR HYDRAULIC CYLINDER   CONTROL VALVE

CHROME NICKEL IRON   LARGE AIR INLETS
END COVERS   FOR QUICK
RESPONSE

BRASS TUBING

CENTRIFUGAL-CAST   "V" RING PISTON   5 STANDARD
TUBING (HONED TO A   PACKING ROD   MOUNTING TYPES
MIRROR FINISH)
COMPOSITION CUP PACKINGS
(SELF-ADJUSTED BY AIR)

Courtesy Logansport Machine Co., Inc.

Fig. 10-2. Use of a compressed air system as the power in conjunction with a hydraulic system as the control in a machine application.

a must in order to avoid damage or breakage of the parts being moved.

Pneumatic systems are considered to be low-pressure systems, while hydraulic systems are considered to be in the high-pressure range. For example, the pressure of a pneumatic system seldom exceeds 150 *psi*. Generally, when the compressed air reaches the functional part of the circuit, the pressure may be only 80 or 90 *psi*, and it is sometimes less. The lower pressure is a result of line losses between the compressor and the circuit; or it may be a result of demands for compressed air elsewhere within the plant.

Hydraulic systems are becoming more common in the pressure ranges up to 5000 *psi*; some systems are available, even to 10,000 *psi*. Most of the systems now in use, however, are in the 500 to 3000 *psi* pressure range. Since hydraulic fluid is only slightly compressible, considerable shock is often encountered in the high-pressure hydraulic systems. The presence of shock may present some types of system problems and malfunctions, if proper provisions are not made to overcome it. Tests show that hydraulic fluid is compressed only approximately one percent when it is subjected to a pressure of 1700 *psi*.

Pneumatic systems are widely used in adverse atmospheres, although some precautions may be necessary to cope with a given situation. Since compressed air does not burn, pneumatic systems are suitable for die-casting equipment, furnaces, and other places where high ambient temperatures are present. In these applications it is recommended that high-temperature packings and seals be installed on the pneumatic components to ensure longer life. Pneumatic systems are ideal for explosive atmospheres, since electrical equipment can be eliminated easily and controls can be either manual or pilot-operated. If it is desirable to use solenoid controls, they can be furnished with explosion-proof characteristics and they are quite inexpensive.

Pneumatic systems are often utilized if a portion of the system is submerged in a fluid such as water. This application may be used to test for leaks in hoses or pressure vessels. In this type of application it is usually desirable for the piston rods of the cylinders to be either chrome plated or made of stainless steel, in order to eliminate any corrosive action of the fluid on the piston rod material.

Pneumatic systems are also commonly employed in extremely dusty atmospheres which can, in many instances, be explosive in nature. These atmospheres are encountered in grain elevators, flour mills, coal mines, etc.

Hydraulic systems also function in adverse atmospheres, but it may be necessary to add rather expensive extra equipment to cope with the adverse condition. For example, if a hydraulic system is used in an explosive atmosphere, an electric motor, switches, controls, and solenoids (if solenoid valves are used) suitable for the type of explosive atmosphere involved are required. In some instances, the hydraulic power unit and motor control are placed in a separate enclosure which can be isolated from the explosive conditions. A standard motor and motor control can then be employed.

If high ambient temperatures and fire hazards are involved, fire-resistant fluids are often used in the hydraulic system. These fluids usually require specially compounded seals and packings. Both the fluid and the seals are more expensive than the standard materials and compounds. These fluids often require the use of a special paint on the interior surfaces of the power unit reservoir and other surfaces that require protection from an adverse reaction of the fluid with the metals. Special care is necessary in the selection of materials and of the mesh size for suction strainers in the power unit.

Hydraulic systems perform satisfactorily in extremely low temperatures only after suitable provisions are made to increase the oil temperature to the correct working level, as discussed in the preceding chapter. On machines that require fine feeds, the hydraulic power unit is often placed in operation in advance of the work shift, so that the oil temperature can be increased to the proper operating temperature before the machine begins to perform the actual work cycle.

Pneumatic systems often encounter difficulties when temperatures are below the freezing point. Condensation may collect in low spots in the air lines; ice is then formed and the air flow is disrupted. In situations where extremely low temperatures are commonly encountered, an antifreeze solution, instead of oil, is sometimes used in the lubricator to prevent the formation of ice; however, this practice has not been found to be entirely satisfactory. Control valves of the solenoid-operated and pilot-operated types become quite sluggish in their operation at low temperatures, because the lubrication congeals and forms a heavy film.

When hydraulic systems are utilized in extremely dirty atmospheres, provisions for keeping as much dirt as possible out of the system are necessary. Dirt enters a system through the various openings in the power device, through the operating mechanisms on the control valves, and between the piston rod and the stuffing box on the cylinders. In unclean atmospheres, it is sometimes necessary to install a large air cleaner on the power unit to assure full atmospheric pressure at all times on the surface of the reservoir fluid. Scrapers, wipers, and boots are often installed on the control valves and cylinders.

The space requirement of the hydraulic system is quite comparable to that of the pneumatic system if the power unit and compressor are not considered. For example, a ½-in. port air control valve is nearly the same in overall size as a ½-in. port hydraulic valve. The hydraulic valve is heavier, since it withstands higher operating pressures. A square covered cylinder used for 150 *psi* air service may be identical in size to a square covered cylinder used for 1500 *psi* hydraulic service. If the required force output of an air cylinder and a hydraulic cylinder are identical, the overall size of the required hydraulic cylinder is somewhat smaller than the overall size of the required air cylinder. In a pneumatic system, the auxiliary equipment, such as regulators, filters, and lubricators, requires some additional space.

Hydraulic systems that are more compact are now being built; they operate at extremely high pressures, and they require only a small space for the force delivered. These units are portable and require only a small quantity of oil.

In many industrial plants, either a single air compressor or a single group of air compressors is commonly used to provide compressed air for all the pneumatic circuits in the entire plant. When hydraulic systems are employed, a hydraulic power unit is used with each circuit or with each group of circuits. The grouping of circuits is often utilized in applications which have lengthy holding cycles, such as a number of molding presses which have time cycles that permit no two presses to demand fluid at the same time.

Leakage should be considered on either system. Internal leakage reduces efficiency and often causes malfunction of controls. External leakage on a hydraulic system becomes a fire hazard, causes slippery conditions that can be dangerous to workmen around machinery, and is detrimental to material processing—especially food, cloth, and synthetic products. Although air leaks in a pneumatic system are easily overlooked and normally do not create housekeeping problems, they are expensive. The cost of compressed air may range between five and fifteen cents per 1000 cubic feet, depending on the size of the installation.

Many users of fluid power equipment do not realize the advantage that can be gained by the utilization of both compressed air and hydraulic fluid in the same circuit. Much research is being conducted in these areas to explore the many possibilities. Some of the advantages are:

1. Effective interlocks can be established; air pressure can be used to operate the smaller devices, such as clamp cylinders, drill (air) motors, etc., and hydraulic pressure can be used to perform the heavier tasks in an automated system.
2. Quick-response air controls can be used to operate large hydraulic control valves which contain air pilot operators.
3. The more expensive hydraulic pilot valves can be replaced with the more inexpensive air pilot valves.
4. Expensive piping from the control panel to the pilot-operated control valves can be eliminated. Plastic tubing performs satisfactorily. This also eliminates considerable assembly time, especially if control panels are involved.

One thing that should always be remembered is: *The two fluids should not be permitted to mix*, since this invariably causes erratic feeds and malfunctions.

REVIEW QUESTIONS

1. List the three general rules for determining whether a pneumatic or a hydraulic system should be used on an application.
2. Which type of fluid system is usually preferable when high speeds are desirable?
3. Which type of fluid system is preferable when low pressures are considered?
4. Compare the two fluid systems in their adaptability for operating in adverse atmospheres.
5. List some of the advantages of combining both compressed air and hydraulic fluid in the same circuit for some applications.

Index

A

Aftercooler, 113
Air compressors, 81-83
  multiple-stage, 82
  single-stage, 82
Air dryers, manual-type, 107-108
Air line lubricators, 104-106
  oil fog, 104
  oil mist, 105-106
Air motor, 24
  air turbine, 24
  piston-type, 24
  vane-type, 24
Air pressure regulator, 41-42
  nonrelieving-type, 41
  relieving type, 41-42
Air turbine, 24
Ambient temperatures, effects of low, 119
Atmospheric pressure, 39-41

B

Bleed-off flow control, 46-47

C

Compressors, air, 81-83
  multiple-stage, 82
  single-stage, 82
Control valves, flow, 37
  directional, 37
  hydraulic, 40
  pneumatic, 40
  pressure, 37
  speed, 37
Cylinder, 16-22
  double-acting, 18
  external construction, 20
  mill-type, 20
  nonrotating, 21-22
  rotating, 21-22
  service media, 18-19
  single-acting, 16
Cylinder-type torque generator, 29-30

D

Diaphragm-type pump, 80-81
Directional control valve operators, 59-70
  manual, 60-63
  mechanical, 67
  pilot, 68-70
  solenoid, 63-67
Directional control valves, 37, 50-54

Directional control valves—cont'd
  disk-type, 50
  four-way, 51
  normally-closed, 50
  normally-open, 50
  plug-type, 50
  poppet-type, 50
  spool configurations, 52
  three-way, 50
  two-way, 50
Double-acting cylinder, 18

F

Filters, 99-104, 108-111
  air line, 99-104
  elements for, 101-103
  guards for, 102-103
  hydraulic, 108-111
  mechanical, 100
Five-way control valve, 53
Flexible piping (hose), 91-95
Flow control valves, 37, 47, 58-59
  hydraulic, 47
  operators, 58-59
Flow controls, 46-50
  bleed-off, 46
  meter-in, 46
  meter-out, 46
  temperature- and pressure-compensated, 48-49
Fluid motor, 22-28
  fixed-displacement, 22, 24
  variable-displacement, 24
Fluid power, associations, 13-15
  uses of, 7
Four-way control valve, 51

G

Gear-type hydraulic motor, 25
Gerotor-type motor, 27-28

H

Hand-type valve operator, 60-62
Heat exchanger, 113, 116
Hose assemblies, 93-97
Hose couplings, 93-98
Hydraulic filters, 108-111
  in intake line, 111
  sump-type, 109
  with warning switch, 110
Hydraulic flow control valve, 47
Hydraulic motor, 25-28

127